PATRICK MOORE'S
BEGINNER'S
GUIDE TO
ASTRONOMY

PATRICK MOORE'S BEGINNER'S GUIDE TO ASTRONOMY

PRC

This edition first published
in 1997 by the
PRC Publishing Ltd,
Kiln House,
210 New Kings Road,
London SW6 4NZ

Copyright © 1997
PRC Publishing Ltd

ISBN 1 85648 437 8

Printed and bound in China

Reprinted 1998 , 1999

PAGE 1: Earth from space.

*PAGES 2 AND 3: Saturn and
six of its satellites.*

RIGHT: Crescent Moon.

A note about the text
To avoid confusion, our
world is always referred to as
the Earth and its companions
the Sun and Moon are
capitalised to differentiate
them from other suns and
moons.

CONTENTS

PREFACE   6

INTRODUCTION   7

THE HISTORY OF ASTRONOMY   9

THE BASICS   13

A TRIP ROUND THE UNIVERSE   21

APPENDICES   57

APPENDIX 1: PLANETS AND THEIR MOONS   57

APPENDIX 2: LIST OF CONSTELLATIONS   71

APPENDIX 3: THE 20 BRIGHTEST STARS   72

APPENDIX 4: THE STAR CHARTS   73

PREFACE
WELCOME TO OUR UNIVERSE!

Hello! I'm Patrick Moore, and I want you to join me in a look around our universe.

Many people believe that to take a real interest in astronomy you need to spend a vast sum of money on a large telescope. I can assure you that this isn't true. Even if you don't want to save up for a telescope, you can still take part in the most exciting exploration left to mankind.

Anyone can take more than a passing interest in the sky by using nothing more than their own pair of eyes!

Do some reading, get a star map and learn your way around the night sky. Join an astronomical society. You will give yourself a lifelong hobby, as I have done myself.

There is a great deal that we still do not know about the universe — even though we have found out so much in recent years. So join me now in this exploration of the heavens.

I wish you all success . . . and clear skies!

INTRODUCTION

This is a book about the universe — by a man who knows his way around it intimately. Patrick Moore is one of the world's most renowned astronomers. From his own particular patch of the universe in southern England, he has spent a lifetime gazing upwards at the heavens.

From him, we have learned about the remarkable changes in the planets and the magical movements of stars. Together with him, we have watched the heavens 'expand' as man's knowledge and technology increase. Through him, thousands of amateur astronomers became hooked on this fascinating subject.

Like myriad generations before us, the sky and its mysteries both fascinate and challenge. For astronomy — the study of everything that lies beyond the Earth's atmosphere — is perhaps the most ancient and magical of all the sciences. Thousands of years ago, the ancients found patterns in the stars and named them after their gods and heroes. They saw stories and myths mirrored in the sky above them and wove their legends into the very fabric of their lives.

Observers began to watch the Sun, Moon and stars and link their movements to events and the passage of time on Earth. The regular rising and setting of the Sun marked the transit of a day; the phases of the Moon from full to new and back to full, took a month. And as the year progressed, different groups of stars appeared in the sky as the seasons moved on.

We have the skies to thank for the creation of time as we on Earth know and comprehend it. The passing centuries have seen many great minds focused on understanding the universe. Much has been discovered. But what still lies beyond those boundaries of space?

It is a subject which will never wane in its mystery and beauty for Patrick Moore and his 'galactic followers'.

Each time Moore talks about the heavens above us, it is with the enthusiasm of a first-time discovery. For what is the point of having high-tech telescopes and equipment at our disposal if we lack passion in our stargazing?

Moore himself, advocates that a trained eye and patience beats technology hands down every time! He also knows the value of 'garden astronomers' and willingly admits:

'Amateur work is genuinely appreciated by professional astronomers, who in some fields rely upon it. Astronomy is still just about the only science in which the amateur can make valuable contributions.'

Now, after his long and learned career, this famed broadcaster and venerable master of science has written an authoritative and fascinating book that introduces the novice to the fabulous world of astronomy.

Here, Patrick Moore explains his passion for 'the sky at night' in the no-nonsense style for which he has become famous. It's a galactic round-up that will capture the imagination of every newcomer — young or old.

The master astronomer dispels many of the various myths and mumbo-jumbo that surround the science. He explains the workings of our own world and those worlds far beyond.

He travels the universe to uncharted galaxies billions of miles away. While on this infinite journey through space, he unveils the sky's many mysteries — from our 'near neighbour', the dusty Red Planet of Mars, to the faraway sinister black holes that could swallow our Earth in an instant.

All such wonders are brought to us in Moore's trademark chatty but gripping style. He is the astronomy expert with the down-to-earth approach to our skies. Patrick Moore brings it all closer to us — by light years!

THE HISTORY OF ASTRONOMY

Astronomy is the oldest science. Cave people, huddled round the fire, would have known the patterns of the stars; they would have watched and used the light from the waxing and waning of the Moon and noticed the occasional bright star that moved erratically.

Evidence from ancient civilisations reveals a highly sophisticated knowledge of the constellations. The night sky was used as a calendar and as a means of navigation. The brightest star in the sky, Sirius, was used by the ancient Egyptians to warn of the flooding of the Nile. The inhabitants of Polynesia and Micronesia in the Pacific Ocean were known to possess extraordinary navigational skills, by using the position of the Sun by day and the patterns of the stars by night.

Records from the Babylonians show they studied the stars in order to watch for any unusual event such as an eclipse of the Sun, when the Moon moves between the Earth and Sun slowly bringing darkness and a few minutes of awe-inspiring night. The Babylonians charted the positions of the Sun, Moon and the five wandering 'stars' (the planets Mercury, Venus, Mars, Jupiter and Saturn), and attempted to predict their future positions.

The actual science of astronomy grew with the Greeks. A succession of great philosophers attempted to explain the motion of the five wanderers. Indeed, the word 'planet' is derived from the Greek word for wanderer.

Observations of the five wanderers showed they did not move uniformly through the sky. They

Ptolemy of Alexandria (c100-178AD) was a Greek astronomer and geographer who lived in Egypt. His greatest work was the Almagest; *in it he expanded and developed Aristotle's theory that the Earth is the centre of the universe around which the Sun, Moon and stars revolve. Ptolemy also drew up a star catalogue that contained the positions and magnitudes of 1,028 stars.*

ABOVE: Nicolaus Copernicus (1473-1543) was a Polish astronomer who postulated the heliocentric system of the Earth and planets rotating around the Sun. The theory took him 30 years to define.

BELOW: Tycho Brahe (1546-1601), a Danish nobleman and astronomer, built two observatories from where he recorded the planet Mars in great detail. His work hugely influenced Johannes Kepler.

stayed within a certain band and moved through the same constellations. But sometimes they moved eastwards, sometimes they would appear to stop, and sometimes they would move backwards, towards the west. This seemingly erratic motion is a consequence of the Earth orbiting the Sun, and the other planets' motion being viewed from a moving platform.

The ancients, however, believed the Earth to be stationary at the centre of the universe, a belief borne out by observation. After all, if you stand and watch, the Sun moves round the Earth from east to west, as do the constellations and the Moon. An observer has no sense at all of the Earth's motion through space.

The Greeks developed many theories to account for the movement of the five wanderers, the most successful being those of Ptolemy, who lived in Alexandria during the second century AD. Ptolemy produced many astronomical works, the most important of which is The *Almagest*. This is a collection of 13 books which covers the movement of the planets and contains a star catalogue based on an earlier work by Hipparchus. Ptolemy's model of the universe, where the planets moved in small circles (epicycles) while moving round the Sun, remained the accepted idea for over a thousand years.

Eventually, however, errors began to creep into Ptolemy's system, compounded over the years by precession (the slow movement of Earth's rotational axis against the background stars). To compensate, astronomers added more and more details to the Ptolemaic system in attempts to maintain the accuracy, but the model became increasingly complicated and inconsistent.

In 1543, Nicholas Copernicus (1473-1543), a Polish astronomer and mathematician, published a treatise entitled *On the Revolutions of the Heavenly Spheres*. In this he proposed that the Earth was a planet, spinning on its own axis and orbiting the Sun in a perfectly circular orbit. With this system, Copernicus did away with the daily motion of the heavens, explained why Mercury and Venus had such a close correlation with the Sun (because they lay between the Earth and the Sun) and solved the puzzling problem of the retrograde motion of the planets. This motion, where the planets appeared to stand still and move backwards in the sky was easily explained if the Earth, along with all the other planets, orbited the Sun.

The German astronomer and mathematician Johannes Kepler (1571-1630) was assistant to Tycho Brahe. He proved that the planets describe elliptical orbits around the Sun and devised three great laws of planetary motion: that the orbit of each planet is an ellipse with the Sun at one of the foci; that the radius vector of each planet describes equal areas in equal times; that the squares of the periods of the planets are proportional to the cubes of their mean distances from the Sun.

Copernicus's work was the first stepping stone to the modern idea of the Solar System. But his theories were very mathematical and not easy even for other scientists to interpret.

In November, 1572, a 'new star' was seen in the constellation of Cassiopeia. This caused great consternation because, ever since the teachings of Aristotle, it had been believed that the heavens were constant and unchanging. Astronomers thus argued that the object could not be a star at all, but something bright, close to the Earth amongst the clouds.

A Danish nobleman, Tycho Brahe (1546-1601), attempted to measure the distance to this new star by observing its motion against the 'fixed' background stars. He failed to determine any such movement and concluded that the star must be at a great distance from the Earth. In fact the star was a supernova, a gigantic explosion of a dying star. The reason Tycho could not measure the star's distance was because the instruments available to him were not sensitive enough. A result of his work, however, was that he was brought to the attention of the Danish king who financed an observatory, called Uraniborg, on the island of Hven, just off the Danish coast.

ABOVE: The Italian physicist and mathematician, Galileo Galilei (1564-1642) made one of the first astronomical telescopes in 1609 and changed scientific thinking for ever.

BELOW: English phycisist, scientist, and astronomer Isaac Newton (1642-1727) was the possessor of one of the greatest scientific minds ever. Amongst his many discoveries was the universal law of gravitation, published 1685.

At Uraniborg, Tycho designed and constructed astronomical instruments which were able to measure the positions of stars with great accuracy. But when he attempted to test out Copernicus's idea of the Earth travelling around the Sun, he failed to do so: his instruments were still not sensitive enough to detect the Earth's motion round the Sun against the background stars.

Tycho's assistant, Johannes Kepler (1571-1630), inherited all Tycho's meticulous observations. Kepler was a mathematician and he spent many years trying to solve the riddle of the motion of the planets. Eventually he realised that the movement of the planets could be easily understood and predicted if all the planets orbited the Sun in ellipses, not circles. With this observation Kepler went on to produce his now famous three laws of planetary motion — three laws which can be applied to any two bodies orbiting each other, not just the planets around the Sun.

While Kepler was studying the tables of Tycho, an Italian physicist was making other dramatic discoveries. Galileo Galilei (1564-1642) was one of the first to use the newly invented telescope to observe the heavens. He saw the phases of Venus and Mercury — a consequence of them orbiting the Sun closer than Earth — and he saw the four brightest moons of Jupiter (now called the Galilean moons) orbiting their parent planet.

These observations suggested a heliocentric solar system. But the Roman Catholic Church attacked Galileo because the theory was not reconcilable with certain passages in the Bible. As a consequence, poor Galileo spent most of his life in open conflict with the Church, and during the latter part of his life he was arraigned before the Inquisition and put under permanent house arrest for his 'vehement suspicion of heresy'. House arrest didn't stop him from writing — his final conclusions on mechanics, *Discourses Concerning Two New Sciences*, was published in 1638 from the Protestant town of Leiden. Galileo died in 1642.

Less than one year afterwards, one of the greatest of Western thinkers, Isaac Newton (1643-1727), was born in England. Newton would go on to use new mathematical techniques to formulate his 'Universal Law of Gravitation' and demonstrate that the planets orbited the Sun according to simple mechanical rules. The story of modern astronomy had well and truly begun . . .

THE BASICS
PLANET EARTH — AND BEYOND

First, let's get the basic facts straight . . . the Earth on which we live is a planet — a globe almost 8,000 miles (12,756km) in diameter. It moves round the Sun, which is a star. That may surprise some people. The Sun is a perfectly ordinary star, and it appears so much larger and hotter than the other stars only because it is so much closer to us.

The distance between the Earth and the Sun is approximately 93 million miles (150 million km). That may sound a long way and, by normal standards, it is — but it isn't far to an astronomer. In astronomy, we have to get used to immense distances and vast spans of time. Nobody can really appreciate them — I certainly can't! — but we just have to accept them.

Planet Earth as seen from space at a point above Africa. Central Africa is covered with clouds, but the Horn of Africa is visible as is the whole of North Africa and the Middle East and most of the Indian Ocean.

The stars are so far away that they look like points of light, and we can't see them in the daytime simply because the sky is too bright. To illustrate just how far away they are, let us take the distance between the Earth and the Sun as just one inch. So how far away is the nearest star? Over four miles away! No wonder that the stars look so much feebler than the Sun, even though some of them are much more powerful.

The Earth isn't the only planet. There are eight others, all moving round the Sun at different distances and in different periods. We take one year to go round the Sun, whereas the innermost planet, Mercury, takes only 88 days.

The Solar System is divided into two well-marked parts. First we have four small, solid planets: Mercury, Venus, the Earth and Mars. Then comes a wide gap, in which move thousands of dwarf worlds which we call asteroids. Then come four giant planets — Jupiter, Saturn, Uranus and Neptune — plus one odd little body, Pluto, which doesn't fit into the general scheme and may not be a proper planet at all.

The planets look like stars and some of them are brilliant; but they have no light of their own and shine only because they are reflecting the rays of the Sun. This is also true of the Moon, which really does go round the Earth and is much the closest body in the sky. We have only one Moon, but other planets have more; Saturn has as many as 18. The Solar System also includes some bodies of lesser importance — notably comets, which can sometimes be spectacular but are very flimsy indeed.

The stars are not really fixed in space. They are dashing about in all sorts of directions at all sorts of speeds but they are so far away from us that, relative to each other, they don't seem to move much over periods of many lifetimes. They form patterns, which we call constellations. Most people can recognise the most famous of all constellations, the Great Bear, part of which is often nicknamed the Plough. The seven stars of the Plough make up an obvious pattern, and it doesn't alter. If you boarded Dr Who's Tardis and went back in time to, say, the Crusades or even the Trojan War, the Great Bear would look just the same. Not so with the planets, which are closer to us. They seem to shift slowly against the starry background from one night to another — and this is how the ancients first realised that they were very different from stars.

Just to stress this, look first at a bird flying at treetop level and then at a jet flying at height. The bird will seem to move the quicker of the two, but of course it doesn't really — I don't think any bird has yet broken the sound barrier! The rule is 'the further, the slower', and the stars are so far away that relative to each other they hardly seem to move at all.

Of course, the whole sky moves round from east to west, but this is only because the Earth is spinning on its axis from west to east. We are observing it all from a moving platform, so to speak.

Before we go any further, we should take a closer look at our own planet. The Earth spins on its axis, in roughly 24 hours. Northward, the axis points to the 'north pole' of the sky — marked by a brightish star, the Pole Star. This means that the Pole Star hardly moves at all and everything else travels round it. If you take a camera at night, point it upward at the Pole Star and take a time exposure, you'll find that the Pole Star remains clear but all the other stars leave trails! If you go to the North Pole, you'll see the Pole Star virtually overhead. Go south of the Equator, and you won't see the Pole Star at all, because it will stay below the horizon. And, in case you wondered, there isn't a bright south pole star.

YOUR OWN TELESCOPE?

Before we go on a trip round the universe, what do we need? Many people believe that to take a real interest in astronomy you need to spend a vast sum of money on a large telescope. Happily this is incorrect, you don't need a big telescope — or even a telescope at all. There is a tremendous amount to be seen with the naked eye or with a pair of binoculars.

Eventually, however, you may think about a telescope. As I have said, it doesn't have to be a big one. I still have the same small telescope I was given when I was 10 years old. That was way back in 1933 and it still works perfectly — even though it cost only £7.

How does a telescope work? Although there are many different sorts, I will explain the two most basic varieties.

In the most common, the refractor telescope, the light from the object you're looking at goes through a glass (or compound) lens, known as an object-glass. The light rays are bunched up and brought to a focus, and the image is enlarged by a second lens known as an eyepiece.

Note that it's the eyepiece which does all the magnification. The role of the object-glass is to collect the light in the first place — and the bigger the object-glass, the more light you can collect. An object-glass 3in across is, in my view, the minimum use-

Example of a 2.5in (60mm) refractor astronomical telescope.

With a refracting telescope the image is formed by the refraction of light through the lens, called the 'object-glass'. The image is then magnified by a lens which is known as the 'eyepiece'.

For anything other than a small telescope, a tripod is absolutely vital to hold the instrument completely steady as even the slightest movement makes viewing impossible.

A WARNING

One thing you must NOT look at directly through any telescope or binoculars is the Sun. It's horribly dangerous. It isn't even safe to stare at it directly with the naked eye.

The Sun is unimaginably hot and bright. Focus the Sun's light and heat onto your eye, and you'll blind yourself permanently. If you turn even a tiny telescope towards the Sun and hold a piece of paper beneath it, it will burst into flame. The same thing would happen with your eye.

The trap is that some small telescopes are sold with dark 'suncaps' over the eyepiece which, it is claimed, make it safe to look directly at the Sun. Believe me, it isn't.

No dark cap can give proper protection. It's apt to shatter without warning, and even a second's exposure will be tragic.

There is only one rule for looking straight at the Sun: DON'T.

ful size. (In fact, rather than get a smaller telescope than that, you should plump for a pair of binoculars.)

There is another kind of telescope which uses mirrors instead of a lens. In the case of these so-called 'reflector' telescopes, the light passes down an open tube and hits a curved mirror. The mirror sends the light back up the tube onto a smaller, flat mirror. This in turn sends the rays into the side of the tube, where an image is formed and enlarged by an eyepiece as before. A telescope with a 6in mirror is about the smallest which is really useful. (Inch for inch, a lens is more effective than a mirror.)

Example of a 6in (152mm) Dobsonian reflector telescope — about the smallest really useful type of astronomical telescope. A reflector uses a concave mirror to magnify the image.

TELESCOPES AND BINOCULARS

BINOCULARS

There are many types of telescopes on the market . . . but before spending a vast amount of money, it is best to buy a good pair of binoculars — these are often better than the cheaper telescopes. There is a great deal of astronomy that can be done with a simple pair of binoculars — and if you discover that astronomy is not for you, then the binoculars will anyway be useful for other hobbies!

Binoculars are normally marked with two numbers, such as 8x40, 7x50 or 10x50. The first number is the magnification, the second is the aperture or diameter of the front lens in millimetres. For general observing, 7x50 or 10x50 are recommended.

Higher magnification binoculars can be useful for specialist astronomy, but a tripod is usually needed to keep the binoculars steady enough to observe through. Also, with increasing aperture, a tripod becomes necessary as the binoculars can get very heavy.

TELESCOPES

There are two basic types of telescope: the refractor and the reflector. The refractor uses lenses to bring an object into focus, where the reflector uses a mirror. There are also types of telescope which use a combination of lenses and mirrors.

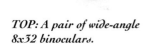

TOP: A pair of wide-angle 8x32 binoculars.

CENTRE: 8x56 binoculars.

BELOW: State of the art, dual-axis, motor drive telescope.

Telescopes are judged not by their magnification but by their aperture. Astronomy is all about looking at faint objects, so the larger the aperture, the more light is collected and the better the view.

The smallest telescopes of any astronomical use at all are refractors of 2–2.5in (50–60mm) and reflectors of about 4in (100mm). These telescopes will show craters on the Moon, the rings of Saturn, the four Galilean satellites of Jupiter and various brighter nebulae and galaxies. They will not be a lot of use for very much else, and indeed a good pair of binoculars will show just as much for less cost.

In general, the smallest useful astronomical telescope is an 3in (80mm) refractor or a 6in (150mm) reflector.

Most telescopes will have their 'f-number' or focal ratio quoted. This is its focal length (the length of the path of light

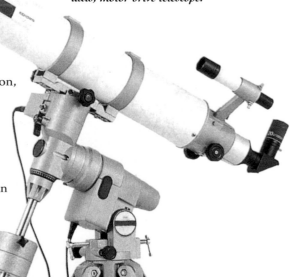

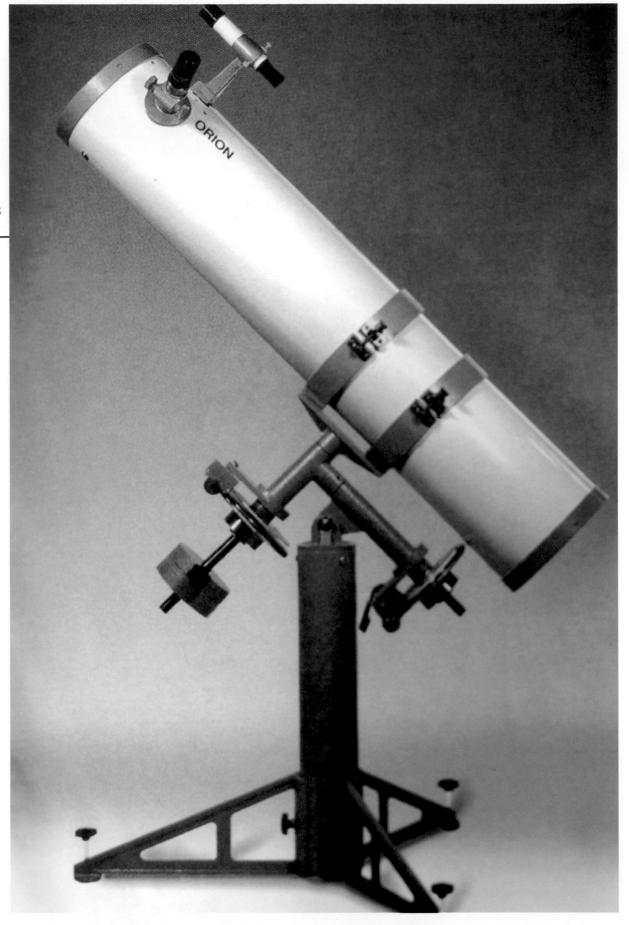

from the main mirror or lens to the eyepiece) divided by its aperture. Thus a telescope with 4in (100mm) aperture and focal length of 31.5in (800mm) is an f/8 telescope. In general, f/4 to f/6 telescopes are preferred by people who like to observe deep sky objects such as galaxies and nebulae, while the larger f-number telescopes (f/7 and above) are preferred by observers of the planets and Moon.

EYEPIECES

It is the eyepiece of a telescope which magnifies the image. Most telescopes will have at least two eyepieces supplied. It is, however, important to realise that it is not possible to use very high-powered eyepieces with small telescopes; too much magnification will give a large, faint and indistinct image.

As a guide, the limiting magnification is about twice the aperture in millimetres. Thus for a 2.3in (60mm) telescope, the highest usable power for an eyepiece is 4.7in (120mm); for an 31.2in (80mm) telescope, it would be 62.4in (160mm), etc.

Eyepieces are usually marked with a number which gives their

FAR LEFT: Although large, this 10in (250mm) telescope is still portable. It is fitted with both electrical and manual drive.

LEFT: A selection of eyepieces to fit various sizes of astronomical telescope.

focal length. To find out the magnification given by a particular eyepiece for a given telescope, the focal length of the eyepiece is divided into the focal length of the telescope. Thus, a one inch (25mm) eyepiece used on a telescope with a focal length of 31.2in (800mm) will give a magnification of x32. A 0.4in (10mm) eyepiece on the same telescope will give a magnification of x80 — but used on a telescope with a focal length of 23.4in (600mm) it will give only a magnification of x60.

THE RIGHT TELESCOPE

The right telescope for you is the one you will use! This can be decided only after experimenting in astronomy — perhaps with a pair of binoculars — and finding out the aspects you enjoy most. One method of experimenting with different types of telescopes and of tapping into a source of expertise is to approach your local astronomical society. Many societies will have a society telescope you can view through, and they will certainly advise you on the best telescope for your requirements.

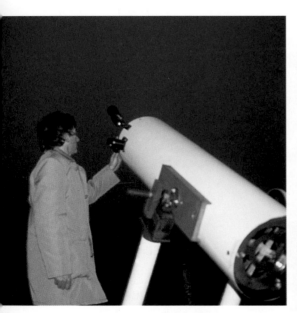

ABOVE and RIGHT: No matter the quality of telescope, the night sky must be clear or all observation is wasted effort.

Always dress warmly, as clear nights mean cold air, and, particularly when standing around, it is very easy to get chilled to the bone. It is a good idea to take a thermos of hot soup or coffee as well.

A TRIP ROUND THE UNIVERSE

OUR NEAREST NEIGHBOUR: THE MOON

It's now time to begin our journey around the universe — and where better to start than with a short step to the Moon, which cosmically is almost on our doorstep . . .

The Moon really is close. Its mean distance from us is less than a quarter of a million miles. Fly 10 times round the Earth, and you'll cover a distance greater than that between the Earth and the Moon. The Moon takes just over 27 days to complete one circuit round the Earth, and of course it shows phases, or apparent changes of shape, from new to full. When it is between the Earth and the Sun, the Moon's daylight side, which is lit by the Sun, is turned away from Earth, and we can't see the Moon at all — this is the true New Moon. As it moves along we start to see a little of the lit side; the Moon becomes a crescent, then a half, and then — when it is on the far side of the Earth with respect to the Sun — it becomes a Full Moon. After that, the phases are repeated in reverse order, and we have the next New Moon.

But what happens if the three bodies are exactly lined up? At New Moon, the Moon will blot out the Sun for a few minutes, causing a solar eclipse — a truly spectacular event.

The Moon is a small world, only just over 2,000 miles (3,218km) across, so it's much smaller than the Earth. Its diameter is only $\frac{1}{400}$ths that of the Sun, but it is 400 times nearer and, by sheer chance, the two bodies appear approximately the same size in the sky

When the Full Moon passes into the shadow cast by the Earth, its

supply of direct sunlight is cut off, and we have an eclipse of the Moon. The Moon doesn't (usually) vanish completely, because some of the Sun's rays are bent on to it by way of the shell of atmosphere surrounding the Earth, but the Moon turns a dim, often coppery colour until it passes out of the shadow again. Eclipses don't happen every month, because the Moon's orbit is tilted, and on most occasions it escapes eclipse.

I've said that the Moon is much smaller than the Earth. It is also less massive. If you could put the Earth in one pan of a gigantic pair of scales, you would need 81 Moons to balance it. This means that the Moon doesn't pull so strongly as the Earth. In other words, its gravity is weaker. This has one important effect: the Moon has hardly any air. To show why, I must tell you a little about something called 'escape velocity'.

If I take a solid body and throw it up, it will rise to a certain height and then fall down. If I throw it faster, it will rise higher before falling back. If I had tremendous muscles and could throw the object up in the air at a speed of 7 miles (11km) per second, which is around 25,000mph (40,225kph), it would never come down at all. The Earth's pull wouldn't be strong enough to hold it, and the object would escape. So 7 miles per second is called the Earth's 'escape into space velocity'.

What's that got to do with the Moon? Well, the air which we breathe is made up of untold millions of tiny particles of air, all flying around at high speeds. If a particle could travel out at 7 miles per second, it would escape. Fortunately, our air particles can't travel as fast as that. But on the Moon, escape velocity is only 1½ miles (2.5km) per second — and that is not enough to hold on to any appreciable atmosphere.

Thus, any air the Moon may once have had, has long since leaked away into space. Today there is no atmosphere there — and therefore no water and no life. All the surface details are sharp and clear-cut . . . no mist, no cloud, no rain, no 'weather'.

Even with the naked eye, you can see details on the Moon. Most obvious are the broad dark plains which we call 'seas' even though there has never been any water in them. We give them romantic names — the Sea of Serenity, the Ocean of Storms, the Bay of Rainbows and so on — because it was once believed that they were true seas.

There are high mountains too, often named after Earth mountains. For instance, the Lunar Apennines, bordering the waterless Sea of Showers; rise to at least 15,000ft (4,575m) above the general level.

But the whole lunar scene is dominated by the craters, which are everywhere. Some of them are well over 100 miles (160km) across and contain tall central mountains within them.

You can see these with any telescope — or good binoculars. But the appearance changes very markedly from night to night. Remember, the Moon shines only by reflected sunlight. A typical crater is a 'walled hole'

FAR LEFT: The shadow of the Earth passes over the face of the Moon.

A TRIP ROUND THE UNIVERSE

23

*The launch of Apollo 11.
Crewed by Neil Armstrong,
Buzz Aldrin and Michael
Collins, it left Earth on
16 July 1969 powered by
a Saturn V rocket driving
five big engines en route for
the first manned landing on
the Moon.*

with a sunken floor. When it is seen as the Sun is rising over it, a crater is wholly or partly filled with shadow. As the Sun goes on rising, the shadow shrinks. And near Full Moon, when the Sun's rays are coming 'straight down' and there are almost no shadows at all, it may be difficult to find the crater. So Full Moon is the very worst time to start looking at it through a telescope. You have much better views of craters when the Moon is at crescent, half or three-quarter phase.

As we all know, the Earth spins round once in 24 hours. The Moon, however, takes just over 27 days. If you are on the Moon, a lunar 'day' is almost as long as two Earth weeks. And the Moon's 'day' is exactly the same length as the time taken for the Moon to go once round the Earth. This means that the Moon keeps the same face turned toward us all the time, and there is part of the Moon that we can never see from Earth.

The simplest way of illustrating what I mean is to stand next to a chair representing the Earth. Think of your head as the Moon — your face being the part of the Moon we can see, and the back of your neck being the part that we can't. Now walk round the chair, turning as you go, to keep looking at the chair. When you've been once round the chair, you will have made one turn on your 'axis' — but anyone sitting on the chair will never have seen the back of your neck! In the same way, from Earth we never see the 'back' of the Moon. Indeed, we had our first views of it only in 1959 — from a spacecraft.

The idea of travel to the Moon is very old but, of course, no ordinary flying machine can take us there. An aircraft can't work unless there is air round it, and there's no air between the Earth and the Moon. Our atmosphere doesn't extend upward for more than a few hundred miles, and the Moon is almost a quarter of a million miles away.

The only answer is to use a rocket, which works by what Isaac Newton called the 'principle of reaction' — that every action has an equal and opposite reaction. Consider a firework rocket. It consists of a hollow tube filled with gunpowder. When you 'light the blue touch-paper and retire immediately', the powder starts to burn. It gives off hot gas, which rushes out of the rocket's exhaust. As it does so, it 'kicks' the rocket in the opposite direction. There is no need for surrounding air. In fact, air is a nuisance, as it has to be pushed out of the way.

I don't suggest building a firework rocket, holding on to the stick and trying to take off! Today we have rocket motors which use liquids and solids, not gunpowder, and can work the vehicle up to the required speed of 7 miles per second, which we need if we're going to reach the Moon.

The first unmanned rockets to reach the Moon were Russian. They were sent up in 1959 and one of them went right round the Moon, sending back pictures of the far side which we can never see from Earth. As we expected, the far side proved to be just as crater-scarred and just as barren as the side we have always known. 10 years later, in 1969, the first men went to the Moon. The spacecraft Apollo 11 carried three astronauts: Neil Armstrong, Buzz Aldrin and Michael Collins. Two of them, Armstrong and Aldrin, landed on the lunar Sea of Tranquillity. Who can forget Neil Armstrong's words as he stepped on to the Moon: 'That's one small step for man, one giant leap for mankind'.

They found a strange world, Aldrin describing the scene as 'magnificent desolation'. On the Moon, a man weighs only ⅙th as much as he does at home, so that in television pictures of that famous lunar walk, everything seemed to happen in 'slow motion'.

Other missions followed. Rocks were brought home from all the Apollo missions to the Moon, the last one being in 1972 — but there was no sign of life, either past or present. The Moon, it seems, has always been sterile. By now we have a good knowledge of the Moon. It is about the same age as the Earth — around 4,500 million years — and most astronomers believe that all the craters were formed aeons ago when it was hit by solid bodies from space.

Before long we should be able to set up a proper Lunar base. This must certainly happen during the 21st century — and I am very ready to believe that some of you, now reading this book, will be able to go there. Meanwhile, do take a telescope or binoculars and look at the Moon's craters, mountains and waterless seas.

ABOVE: The definitive photograph of Buzz Aldrin standing on the Moon's surface, taken by Neil Armstrong.

BELOW: Apollo 16's Lunar Rover allowed astronauts to travel some way from their spacecraft.

OUR VERY OWN STAR:
THE SUN

Now let's turn to — but not look at — the Sun itself. The Sun is very hot indeed — even the surface temperature is not far short of 10,832°F (6,000°C) — and it is also very large. Its diameter is 865,000 miles (1,400,000km). That's more than 100 times greater than that of the Earth. You could pack a million globes the volume of the Earth inside the Sun — and still leave room to spare.

As I have already warned, if you focus the Sun's light and heat onto your eye, you'll blind yourself permanently. However, there is a way to look at the sun without harming your eyesight. Point the telescope at the Sun without putting your eye anywhere near the eyepiece and project the Sun's image onto a screen held or fastened behind the eye-end. You'll see the Sun's disk well — and you may see dark patches known as sunspots.

These spots aren't really black; they look dark only because they are around 3,632°F (2,000°C) cooler than the surrounding surface. You don't always see them. Every 11 years or so, the Sun becomes very active and there may be many groups of spots. At other times, the Sun is quieter, and there may be many spotless days.

The Sun spins on its axis in about 3½ weeks. So, if you plot the spots from day to day, you will see them being carried across the Sun's face. It's always worth doing — and a bonus is that you can do it in the daytime!

The Sun isn't burning in the same way as a coal fire. A Sun made up of coal, burning as fiercely as the real Sun actually does, wouldn't last for long on the cosmological scale — and we know that the Sun is older than the Earth, which itself is 4,500 million years old. The Sun shines because of what we call 'nuclear transformations' going on inside it, near the centre of the globe where the temperature is at least 25 million°F (14 million°C) and the pressure is colossal.

The most plentiful substance in the universe is hydrogen — after all, water is made up partly of hydrogen (a water-molecule is made up of two atoms of hydrogen and

The Sun in H-alpha.

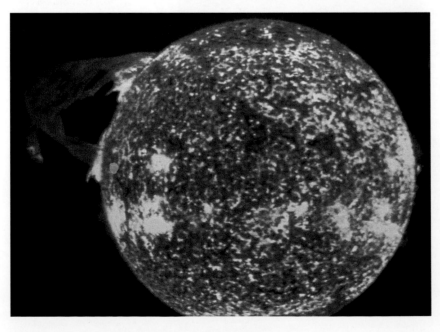

one atom of oxygen: H_2O). Over 70 percent of the Sun is made up of hydrogen (chemical symbol H) and, near the core, strange things are happening: the 'bits' of hydrogen are running together to build up 'bits' of a heavier gas, helium (chemical symbol He). It takes four 'bits' of hydrogen to make one 'bit' of helium, and each time this happens a little energy is set free and a little mass — or weight, if you like — is lost. And that's the energy which keeps the Sun shining. The total mass-loss amounts to 4,000,000 tons per second — imagine the weight of four million coal trucks! But don't be alarmed; the Sun is so huge that it won't change much for several thousands of millions of more years. This, then, is the basic building block of the sun, the transformation of H to He.

Most of what we know about the Sun has been learned by using instruments based on the principle of the spectroscope, an instrument for 'splitting up' and analysing light rays. What we usually call 'white' light isn't really white at all — it is made up of a combination of all the colours of the rainbow, from red through orange–yellow–green–blue–indigo–violet. If you pass a beam of sunlight through a glass prism, or something which acts in the same way, you will split it up into a coloured band. Crossing this band are dark lines. Each dark line is due to one particular substance — and so we can tell of what substances the Sun is made.

You remember my telling you that sometimes, at New Moon, the Moon passes straight in front of the Sun and causes a total eclipse? When this happens, we can see the Sun's outer atmosphere, and the sight is magnificent. Round the Sun's edge can often be seen masses of red hydrogen which we call prominences, and beyond these comes the glorious pearly corona, which spreads out in all directions.

If you have the chance to see a total eclipse, don't miss it. The problem is that the Moon's shadow is only just long enough to reach the Earth, so that you have to be in just the right place at just the right time. We always know when eclipses are going to happen — the last total eclipse visible from England was in 1927 and the next will be on 11 August 1999. We'll have to travel to Cornwall to see that, though the track also crosses the Channel Islands and parts of Europe.

If the eclipse is only partial, we can't see the prominences and the corona. The Moon's path round the Earth is not quite circular. If the lining-up happens when the Moon is furthest from us, the Moon is not quite big enough to cover the Sun, so that a ring of sunlight is left showing. This is called an annular eclipse (from the Latin *annulus*, a ring).

Using spectroscopic equipment, we can now see the prominences at any time, and we can take films of their motions. They can shift very rapidly indeed. But this does need special equipment — and again I say: ***Be careful***. I don't apologise for stressing this, because it is so important. You have only one pair of eyes and they aren't renewable.

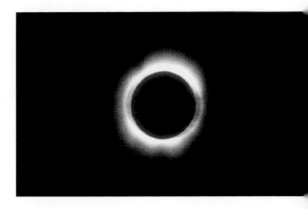

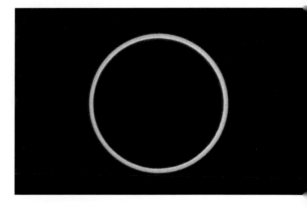

TOP: A rare event — the total eclipse of the Sun.

ABOVE: An annular eclipse of the Sun occurs when the Moon passes in front of the Sun but because of the differing distances between the Sun, Moon and Earth, the Moon cannot completely cover the Sun's disk, instead leaving a bright ring of light around the circumference.

OUR 'FAMILY': THE PLANETS

MERCURY

The Sun is the ruler of the Solar System — so let's remind ourselves of his family, and take a brief look at them one by one. If we work 'outwards' from the Sun, we come first to Mercury, which many people have probably never seen! It's small — only 3,000 miles (4,827km) across, closer in size to the Moon than the Earth. It's also quite a long way away — it's a mere 36 million miles (58 million km) from the Sun on average, and speeds round in a mere 88 days. The problem is that it is always in the same part of the sky as the Sun, so with the naked eye you can see it only when it is at its lowest — either low in the west after sunset, or low in the east before dawn. Look for it by all means, but don't sweep around with binoculars until the Sun is completely below the horizon, otherwise you might look at the Sun by mistake.

Because Mercury is closer to the Sun than we are, it shows phases similar to those of the Moon, and for much the same reason (bearing in mind that Mercury goes round the Sun, not round the Earth). It may show up as a crescent or half, although when full it's on the far side of the Sun so it won't be visible. Very occasionally, when new, it may pass in front of the Sun and show up as a black spot. This is called a transit, and the next time it happens will be in 1999.

Because Mercury is particularly small and lightweight, it has very little atmosphere.

Mercury from Mariner 10.

One spacecraft has passed by it — Mariner 10 in 1973 and 1974 — and sent back pictures showing a rocky, cratered landscape very like that of the Moon. The days are hot on Mercury, where the surface temperature rises to hundreds of degrees. But the nights are bitter and very long, because the planet is a slow spinner. I can't imagine that anyone will go there in the foreseeable future but if they could, they would find a barren, scorching landscape under a black sky. Still, it's worth looking for Mercury just for the fun of finding it, and yearly almanacs will tell you when and where in the sky to search for it.

VENUS

Planet number two, Venus, is as different from Mercury as it could possibly be, and you can't mistake it for anything else because it is so brilliant. Like Mercury, it shows up in the west after sunset or the east before sunrise, but it looks almost like a small lamp, and it can cast shadows. This is partly because it is bigger than Mercury — almost exactly the same size as the Earth — and partly because it is nearer. At its closest, it is only about 100 times as far away as the Moon, and of course it shows phases from new to full. It doesn't often pass in transit across the face of the Sun. It last did so in 1882, and won't do so again till 2004, so that there can be nobody now living who has ever seen a transit of Venus.

But though Venus and Earth are near-twins, they are not identical twins. Look at Venus through a telescope and all you'll see will be the top of a layer of clouds.

A sinuous volcanic channel on Venus.

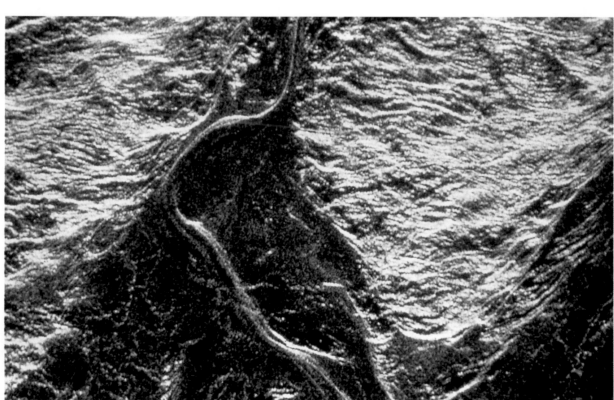

Composite of Venus in
radio.

We can't see through the clouds, so there's no such thing as a clear day on Venus. The atmosphere is different from ours, being made up chiefly of the heavy gas carbon dioxide, and those shining clouds are rich in sulphuric acid. Add the fact that the surface temperature is getting on for 1,000°F (480°C). and that the pressure is at least 90 times that of our air (at sea level), and you'll realise that Venus is not a very pleasant place.

The Russians have landed automatic probes there, and sent back pictures of the surface, but our best maps have been made by using radar-carrying spacecraft. The latest spacecraft to visit Venus was Magellan, which has shown us towering peaks and huge volcanoes that may be active. Venus may have had seas once, but they have long since evaporated. I am quite sure that nobody will go there in our time. Venus is odd in many ways. It spins very slowly 'the wrong way', so from Venus the Sun rises in the west and sets in the east 243 Earth-days later. This is longer than Venus's own 'year' of nearly 225 Earth-days. All in all, the differences seem to stem from the fact that Venus is over 20 million miles closer to the Sun than we are.

MARS

Passing by the Earth, we come next to Mars, the so-called Red Planet. It really is red, which is why it was named after the God of War. Mars is smaller than the Earth but larger than the Moon. It takes 687 Earth-days to go round the Sun, and its own 'day' is only just over half an hour longer than ours. Telescopes show a red disk with white icecaps at the poles and dark markings which were once thought to be seas, but are now known to be areas where the red, dusty stuff has been blown away by winds in the thin Martian atmosphere, exposing the darker surfaces below.

Years ago, astronomers believed they could see streaks on Mars which were taken to be canals, built by the Martians — whatever they might be! — in a vast irrigation system. But, alas, the canals don't exist. They were simply tricks of the eye.

ABOVE: The planet Mars taken by Viking 2.

BELOW: Asteroid Gaspra taken by spacecraft Galileo.

Spacecraft have flown past Mars and sent back pictures showing craters, plains, valleys and huge volcanoes, one of which, Olympus Mons, is three times the height of our Everest and is crowned by a 40-mile (65km) crater. Then, in the 1970s, Viking spacecraft made controlled landings there, mainly to search for any signs of life. But — probably because the atmosphere is so thin and is made up of carbon dioxide — they didn't find any.

Using the Viking results, we can at least go on a trip over the Martian surface — and it will be spectacular by any standards! In the 21st century I am sure we will set up manned bases there. But one thing we can never do is to go out into the open unprotected by space suits. We can never turn Mars into a second Earth.

Mars has two moons, called Phobos and Deimos. Both are very small — less than 30 miles (50km) across for Phobos, even less for Deimos — and they wouldn't be of much use in lighting up the dark Martian nights. Probably they are not genuine moons, but asteroids 'captured' from the swarm which lies beyond Mars.

These asteroids are curious little worlds. None is large enough to have any air. Only one (Ceres) is as much as 500 miles (800km) across, and only one (Vesta) can ever be seen without a telescope; even then it looks just like a star. Spacecraft have brought back pictures of a few asteroids, and we now believe that they are debris 'left over' when the main planets were formed from a cloud of dust and gas surrounding the young Sun.

JUPITER

So far, we have looked at the smaller planets close to the Sun. Now we move 'outwards' to the giants — beginning with Jupiter. There's never any problem in finding Jupiter, because it is big and brilliant — brighter than any other star or planet apart from Venus. It is almost 90,000 miles (145,000km) across, extremely large relative to the Earth.

Jupiter isn't solid and rocky. Use a telescope and you will see that it has a yellowish, flattened disk crossed by streaks which we call cloud belts. The surface is made up of gas, mainly hydrogen, and it is very cold. Deep inside the globe there is probably a hot core, surrounded by layers of liquid hydrogen beneath the clouds which we can see.

Though Jupiter takes nearly 12 years to go round the Sun, it spins on its axis in less than 10 hours. This explains why it's flattened: centrifugal force making its equator bulge out. Through any small telescope, Jupiter is a fine sight, and you may even see the great Red Spot, which is a whirling storm with a surface area greater than the Earth's.

We have sent spacecraft to Jupiter, and the two Voyagers, which by-passed the planet in 1979, sent back superb views. They also told us that Jupiter is a dangerous world! It is surrounded by zones of deadly radiation which would instantly kill any astronaut foolish enough to venture too close. There is also an extremely strong magnetic field and the surface is in a state

Jupiter and Galilean moon montage.

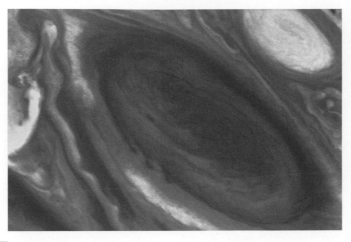

of constant turmoil, with thunder and lightning. No, we'll never go to Jupiter.

But Jupiter isn't alone. It has four large moons: Io, Europa, Ganymede and Callisto. Three of these are larger than the Moon, and Ganymede is actually larger than the planet Mercury. You can see them with any small telescope, or even good binoculars. Of the satellites, Ganymede and Callisto are cratered and icy, Europa is smooth, but Io has a red surface with active volcanoes. Since Io also moves inside Jupiter's lethal radiation zones, it must be just about the deadliest world in the Solar System.

SATURN

Beyond Jupiter lies Saturn, second of the giant planets, smaller than Jupiter but (with a diameter of 70,000 miles/112,500km) still much larger than Earth. In make-up, Saturn is not unlike Jupiter but it is distinguished by its set of icy rings. To me, Saturn is the loveliest object in the sky and, when the rings are well placed, a small telescope shows them well. However, though they measure almost 170,000 miles (273,500km) from end to end, they are less than a mile thick — and when they lie edgewise-on to us, as they did in 1995, they almost vanish.

ABOVE: Jupiter's Great Red Spot.

BELOW: Saturn and six satellites.

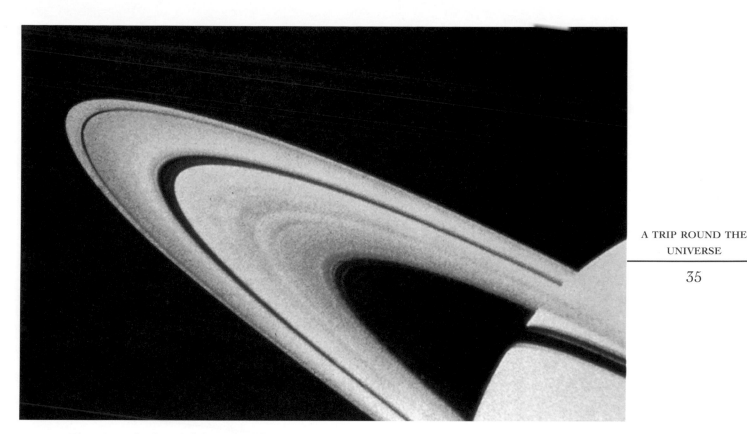

The rings look solid but they aren't. Saturn's powerful gravity would quickly pull any solid or liquid ring to pieces. The rings are made up of tiny pieces of ice, all spinning round Saturn like tiny moons, forming many hundreds of ringlets and narrow divisions. All the giant planets have rings, but only Saturn's are bright. In 1980 and 1981 the two Voyager spacecraft relayed back superb views of them.

The famous and beautiful rings of Saturn.

Saturn takes almost 30 years to round the Sun, at a mean distance of 887 million miles (1,400 million km), so it takes a spacecraft a long time to get there. But there are also the satellites — 18 in all, although only one of them, Titan, is large. With a small telescope, you can see it as a star-like point. Titan has a thick atmosphere, but we couldn't breathe it, and the temperature is very low. The Voyager pictures show the top of a layer of orange 'smog'. We aren't sure what Titan is like underneath the clouds, and it is thought that there may be an ocean down there — although a chemical ocean rather than a watery one. With luck, we'll find out in 2004, because a special unmanned spacecraft is scheduled to make a controlled landing there. All Saturn's other satellites are much smaller and are icy. One of them, Iapetus, has one side as bright as snow and the other which is blacker than a blackboard! From Iapetus, Saturn would be a marvellous sight.

URANUS AND NEPTUNE

Beyond Saturn there are two more giant planets: Uranus and Neptune. You can just see Uranus with the naked eye if you know where to look for it but to see Neptune you need a telescope.

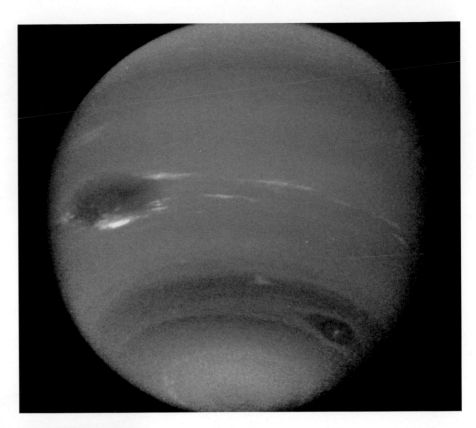

RIGHT: *Neptune from Voyager.*

BELOW: *Neptune's rings.*

BOTTOM: *Uranus in visible and false colour (right).*

FAR RIGHT: *Composite picture of Uranus with Miranda in foreground.*

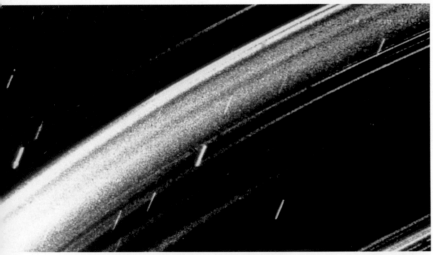

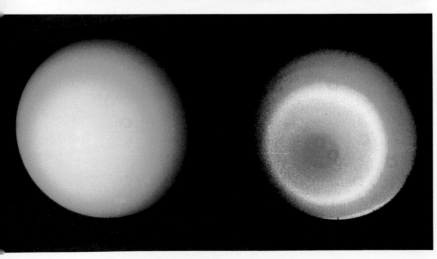

Both Uranus and Neptune have been passed by the same spacecraft, Voyager 2, which was launched from Cape Canaveral in 1977. By sheer good luck, at the end of the 1970s the four giant planets were strung out in a curved line, so that Voyager 2 could pass by them one after the other — Jupiter in 1979, Saturn in 1981, Uranus in 1986 and finally Neptune in 1989.

After that epic 'photo-call', Voyager began a never-ending journey out of the Solar System. It will never come back and, although we are still in radio contact with it, before long we'll lose touch and will never know what eventually happens to it as it travels out on its epic journey.

The outer giants are much smaller than Jupiter or Saturn, but still much larger than Earth. They too have gaseous surfaces and darkish ring systems. Uranus is rather bland, but Voyager showed dark patches on Neptune. And Neptune's main satellite, Triton, proved to have poles covered with pink nitrogen snow. Triton is so cold that nitrogen, which is gaseous in our air, freezes out. In its pink polar cap are active geysers, which were totally unexpected.

PLUTO

Finally, on the edge of the planetary system, is Pluto, discovered in 1930 by my old friend Clyde Tombaugh. Pluto looks like a star in ordinary telescopes but is hardly worth ranking even as a proper planet, because it is very small — smaller even than our Moon.

Pluto has a very thin atmosphere and probably an icy surface. It is so far away that it takes 248 years to go round the Sun, but it has a strange path, and when closest-in, it is actually nearer than Neptune. Not until 1999 will it again pass beyond Neptune's path. Unfortunately, no spacecraft have been anywhere near Pluto, although our best telescopes have shown it has a companion, Charon.

Artist's impression of the Sun from Pluto and Charon.

SPACE HIGHWAYS

COMETS

Among the large numbers of very small bodies in the Solar System are comets and meteoroids. A comet isn't solid and rocky in the same way as a planet. A typical comet has any icy centre, mixed in with 'rubble', never more than a few miles across. Most comets move round the Sun in long, narrow paths — some of them in periods of a few years, though others take so long that they come near us only once in many lifetimes, and we can't predict them. When a large comet nears the Sun, its ices start to 'boil off', and the comet's centre is surrounded by a 'head' and often a tail or tails. As the comet moves outward again and cools, the head and tail disappear. Tails always point more-or-less away from the Sun, so that an outward-moving comet travels tail first. This is because the tiny particles in the tail are 'driven out' — the dust particles by what we call the solar wind, and gas particles by the pressure of sunlight. Some comets have tails of both kinds, though others never develop tails at all.

The comet Hyakutake, travelling through the night sky.

HALLEY'S COMET

The only bright comet which we see regularly is Halley's — so named because it was Edmond Halley, Britain's second Astronomer Royal, who first realised that it comes back predictably. It takes 76 years to go round the Sun and was last near us in 1986, though it wasn't then well placed and was never as bright as it had been in 1835 and 1910. However, a spacecraft, *Giotto*, went through its head and sent back close-range pictures of the nucleus, which was shaped like a peanut and was less than 20 miles (32km) long. Halley's Comet has been seen regularly for many centuries. For example, it was here in 1066, just before the Battle of Hastings, and is shown in the Bayeux Tapestry; it was regarded by the Saxons as an evil omen, and

King Harold is shown toppling on his throne! It will be here again in 2061 — I'm afraid I won't see it, but perhaps you will . . .

METEORS

A comet is a body travelling far beyond the Earth's air, and it doesn't move perceptibly against the stars as seen with the naked eye. If you see something moving quickly, it can't be a comet. It may be an artificial satellite, but if it is very fast it will almost certainly be a meteor.

As a comet travels round the Sun, it leaves a dusty trail behind it. If we go through one of these trails, we 'pick up' tiny pieces of debris. If a particle dashes into the Earth's upper air, moving at anything up to 45 miles per second, it rubs against the air particles and becomes so heated by friction that it burns away in the streak of radiation that we call a shooting star. That is all a shooting star is: a tiny piece of 'dust' burning away in the atmosphere. By the time it has dropped to around 40 miles (65km) above the ground, it has burned away completely.

Many meteors produce 'showers'. The meteors in any particular bunch are moving through space at the same rate at the same speed, and so seem to come from one particular point in the sky, known as the radiant — just as parallel lanes of a motorway will seem to meet at a distant point if you look at them from a bridge. There are many showers each year, but the richest of them is seen during the first two weeks of August. At that time look up into a dark, clear sky and you should see several meteors within a few minutes, sometimes a spectacular show.

METEORITES

Meteors are so small and flimsy that they burn away harmlessly. But now and then the Earth is hit by a larger body, which may strike the ground intact, this is then called a meteorite. Note that there is no connection between a meteorite and a shooting-star meteor; meteors are cometary debris, while meteorites probably come from the asteroid belt. We know of many meteorite craters — there's a famous one near Flagstaff, Arizona, almost a mile (1.6km) wide, formed when a meteorite, theorised as being only c11yd (10m) across, hit the desert well over 20,000 years ago.

There is always the chance of another major hit, and it could cause great damage. It has even been suggested that this did happen around 65 million years ago, and then threw up so much debris that the climate was changed — and the dinosaurs, which had been lords of the world for so long, died out. This may or may not be true, but at least it is a possibility. And we have seen one major impact in very recent times. In 1994 a comet was observed to hit Jupiter and destroy itself. Fortunately the Earth is a small target and the chances of any major disaster in the foreseeable future are very slight — so please don't worry!

THE STARS

Up to now we've been talking about our own local part of the Universe, but now it's time to look further afield — to the stars. Remember, every star is a sun, and our Sun is an ordinary star.

I've already said that the stars are very distant — so far that it would be awkward to measure their distances in miles, just as it would be awkward to give the distance between London and Sydney in inches. Instead, we use the light-year. Light doesn't travel instantaneously. It flashes along at 186,000 miles (300,000km) per second — so in a year it covers almost 6 million million miles (9.5 million million km). This is what we call the light-year. It takes 1¼ seconds for light to travel to us from the Moon, 8½ minutes to reach us from the Sun — but over four years from the nearest bright star, Alpha Centauri in the southern sky!

I'm afraid it would take too long for me to give you a 'tour' of the constellations, but believe me it doesn't take long to learn your way around, because the patterns do not change. My method is to select a few prominent constellations and use these as 'guides' to the rest.

Orion. This photograph took a three-minute driven exposure on 400ASA film.

You can hardly mistake the Great Bear, or Plough, which never sets over Britain. The two end stars of the pattern show the way to Polaris, the Pole Star in the Little Bear; the Bear's tail points towards the brilliant orange star Arcturus in the constellation of Boötes, the Herdsman.

In winter we have Orion, with two very brilliant stars, Betelgeuse and Rigel. The three stars of the Belt point downward to Sirius in the Great Dog — the brightest star in the sky — and upward to the orange Aldebaran, in the Bull.

Of course, the constellation patterns are quite arbitrary, because the stars are at very different distances from us and the stars in any particular constellation aren't connected with each other. We are simply dealing with the effects of our own line of sight. The constellations have been named for may hundreds, even thousands of years.

When I was a boy, I obtained an outline star map and made a pious resolve to identify one new constellation every clear night. Before long, I had assembled a good working knowledge. After all, there are only a few thousands of stars visible with the naked eye.

Even a casual glance will show that the stars are not all alike. Not only are they different in brightness, but also in colour, and some stars are clearly orange or red (such as Betelgeuse in Orion, whereas the other leader of Orion, Rigel, is white). These variations indicate real differences in surface temperature. Thus the white Rigel has a temperature of over 18,000°F (10,000°C) at its surface and is hotter than our yellow Sun (at below c10,900°F/6,000°C) whereas the surface temperature of Betelgeuse is only half this. However, to make up for this, Betelgeuse is very large. Its diameter is around 250 million miles (400 million km), so that it could swallow up the whole path of the Earth round the Sun. It is 15,000 times as luminous as the Sun. But that is puny compared with Rigel, which could match 60,000 Suns!

To find out a star's power, we must know its distance, and that's not easy. The very closest stars can have their distances measured by what we call parallax — the same, essentially, as the method used by a surveyor to measure the distance of some

BELOW: Chart showing the major stars in Orion.

BOTTOM: This diagram shows the relative sizes of the different types of stars.

FAR LEFT, TOP: Orion as photographed from a light-polluted area, and BELOW in a dark sky. Both taken on 400ASA film. .

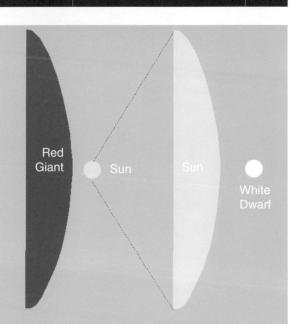

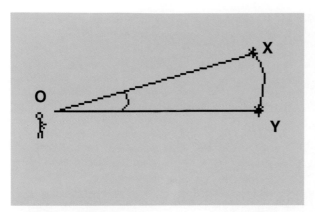

ABOVE: The angular distance (or apparent distance) between two stars X and Y, as seen by the observer O, is the angle YOX. This angle is precisely expressed in degrees, minutes and seconds of arc.

BELOW: A useful rough guide to the angular distance of the stars can be determined by comparing parts of the hand held at arm's length to the stars in the sky.

inaccessible object such as a mountain-top. He measures the angle of the object as seen from the opposite ends of a baseline, and from this he can work out the whole triangle — and hence the distance of the peak. For the stars, we use the Earth's orbit as a baseline. Observe a closer star first in January and then in June; the baseline now is twice the Earth's distance from the Sun, which is 186 million miles (300 million km). The nearby star will show a parallax shift, and its distance can be found.

The shifts are very small, however, and beyond a few hundred light-years they are swamped in unavoidable errors of observation. So we have to turn back to the spectroscope. I've already said something about the spectrum of the Sun — a rainbow band crossed by dark lines, each of which is the trademark of some particular substance (such as hydrogen, oxygen or iron). Stars with different temperatures have different types of spectra but by studying them we can have a good idea of how powerful the star really is. We can also find out what substances exist there. And from this we can work out how a star evolves.

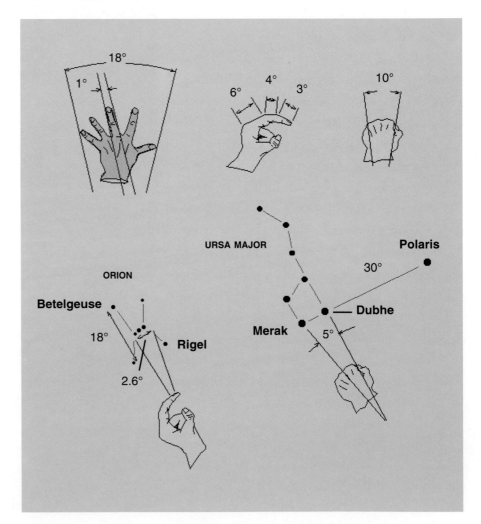

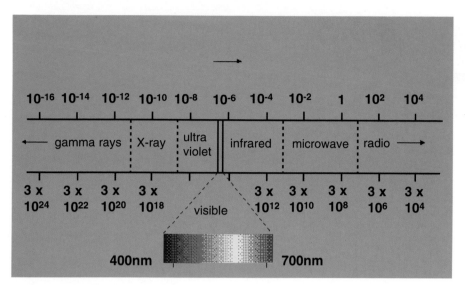

The electromagnetic spectrum. Visible light is only part of the electromagnetic spectrum which varies from highly energetic gamma rays down to long-wavelength low-energy radio waves.

A TRIP ROUND THE
UNIVERSE

45

Now let's concentrate on the stars we can see from Planet Earth. Some stars are members of pairs, such as Mizar in the Great Bear. Look at it with the naked eye and you will see a much fainter star, Alcor, close beside it. Use a telescope and you'll see that Mizar itself is made up of two components, one brighter than the other. Together they make up what we call a binary system.

Many thousands of binary systems are known. Indeed, binary pairs may be commoner than single stars such as the Sun. If the two components are equal, they will move together round their common centre of gravity, rather in the manner of the two bells of a dumbbell when you twist them by the bar joining them. If one component is more massive than the other, the centre of gravity will be closer to the heavier star.

A small telescope will show many doubles, some of them with contrasting colours. One of these is called Albireo, in the constellation of the Swan. The brighter star is golden yellow,while its companion is vivid blue. I never tire of looking at it.

Some binaries show changes in brightness — not because they really alter, though. One of these is called Algol, in the constellation Perseus. The brighter star has a fainter companion. Every two and a half days, the companion passes in front of the brighter star and blots out part of its light, so that Algol gives a long, slow 'wink'. It fades for four hours, stays faint for 20 minutes and then recovers — but it is always easy to see with the naked eye. Many other Algol-type stars are known.

Some stars are genuinely variable, and brighten and fade over short periods because they are pulsating. Betelgeuse in Orion is one of these. There are also stars which suddenly brighten up and become prominent for a few days, weeks or even months before passing back into obscurity. We call these novæ. Don't confuse a nova with a supernova. In a nova, the outburst dies away and doesn't damage the star, whereas in a supernova outburst the star blows itself to bits.

LIFE AND DEATH OF A STAR

A star begins by condensing out of a cloud of dust and gas. Gravity makes it shrink. It heats up inside. Temperature and pressure rise until nuclear fusion begins . . . and only then is it a star. (Until that stage of nuclear fusion, it is known as a proto-star.) Unless, that is, it is too low in mass, when it simply shines feebly as a red dwarf before losing all its light and heat.

A Sun-like star shines steadily for a very long time — thousands of millions of years in the case of the Sun — but when it starts to run short of hydrogen fuel, things really begin to happen! It starts to use different nuclear reactions, and becomes a red giant. When this happens to the Sun, the Earth will be destroyed, I'm afraid. But don't worry; this is not going to happen for around 4,000 million years yet!

Next thing is that the star throws off its outer layers, and becomes what we call a planetary nebula (a bad name, as it has nothing to do with a planet and is not a true nebula). The outer layers dissipate and what is left of the star shrinks to become a very small, very dense object called a white dwarf. All its atoms are crushed and broken, so that you could pack a ton of white dwarf material into an egg cup. The best-known white dwarf is the tiny companion of Sirius, which is as massive as the Sun but is only about three times the diameter of the Earth.

After a very long period indeed, the star becomes a cold, dead globe.

That's the story of a star such as our Sun. If the original star is much more massive, it will die more spectacularly. When it runs out of fuel, it collapses. There is an implosion, followed by a rebound, and the star blows itself to pieces in what we call a supernova outburst.

This doesn't happen often, but in 1987 one of these explosions happened in the companion galaxy to our Milky Way, visible from the Southern Hemisphere system, called the

BELOW: Close-up of star forming region in the Eagle Nebula.

BOTTOM: Star forming region in the Eagle Nebula.

Large Megallanic Cloud. It became visible with the naked eye for a time. At its peak, it matched the output of several thousands of millions of Suns.

During a supernova, the star blows itself to pieces — and we are left with an expanding gas-cloud, inside which is a tiny remnant even denser than a white dwarf. Back in the year 1054, a supernova flared up in the constellation of the Bull, and we can still see its debris. We call it the Crab Nebula. A small telescope shows its remains as a misty patch, though you need a large telescope to photograph its details.

BLACK HOLES

If the original star is more massive still when the collapse of the star's core starts, the event is so violent and so catastrophic that nothing can stop it. The star shrinks and shrinks, becoming denser and denser and pulling more and more strongly. Finally, it is pulling so strongly that not even light can escape from it — and if light can't do so, then nothing else can, because light is the fastest thing in the Universe. The old star has surrounded itself with a 'forbidden area' which can swallow up material, but from which nothing can escape. It has become a black hole.

Obviously we can't see a black hole, and we have to detect it because of its effects on objects close to it which we can see. What happens to the old star? I'm afraid I can't tell you — because nobody knows. Unquestionably, black holes are the most bizarre objects in the entire Universe.

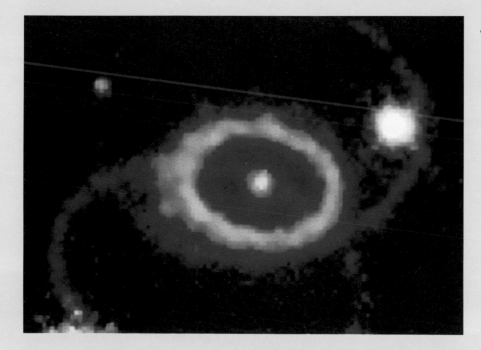

Supernova 1987A.

Map of the constellation of Orion. This is an easily identifiable group and its major stars can be used as pointers to other interesting stars in the sky.

Orion is located at the celestial equator at 5h 30m right ascension, 0° declination.

Some variable stars are particularly useful because they 'give away' their real luminosities by the way in which they behave. These are known as Cepheid variables, because the first to be identified was the star Delta Cephei in the far northern sky.

I have told you about the constellations — but what about their names? The ancients saw patterns in the sky, and drew on these stars their favourite mythological figures . . .

Orion was a mighty hunter who boasted that he could kill any creature on Earth. But he forgot the Scorpion, which crawled out of a hole in the ground, stung him in the heel and killed him. When the gods brought Orion back to life and placed him in the heavens, the Scorpion was put there too — as far away from Orion as possible, so that the two can never meet again!

The best-known legend is that of the princess and the sea monster. A proud queen, Cassiopeia, boasted that her daughter Andromeda was more beautiful than the sea-nymphs. This annoyed the sea god, who sent a monster, Cetus, to ravage the kingdom. To placate the god, Andromeda was chained to a rock by the seashore to be gobbled up by the monster. Mercifully, the situation was saved by the hero Perseus, who had been on an expedition to kill the Gorgon Medusa, a hideous creature with a woman's head and hair made of snakes, her glance would turn any living thing to stone. Mounted on winged sandals, Perseus turned the monster to stone by showing it the Gorgon's head, and then, in the best tradition of mythology, married the beautiful princess. The Gorgon's head is marked by Algol, the winking 'demon star' . . .

The princess's father was Cepheus — and it is here that we find the famous star Delta Cephei. It's very luminous (over 6,000 Sun-power) and it has a period of just over five days; that is to say it takes five days to pass from one maximum to the next. We have found that any other similar star with the same period will have the same luminosity. If the period is longer, the luminosity will be greater. In fact, we can tell the power of a Cepheid merely by watching it, and we can then find its distance. Very useful!

Stars often occur in clusters, the most famous being that of the Pleiades or Seven Sisters, not far from Orion. The whole cluster contains hundreds of members but you can see at least seven stars with the naked eye. There are many other open clusters, too, such as the 'Beehive' cluster Praesepe in the constellation of the Crab. Other clusters are different, and are globular in form — such as the cluster in the constellation Hercules, which you can just see with the naked eye as a tiny patch. Using a telescope resolves it into stars.

Globular clusters lie round the edge of our main star-system. They contain the useful Cepheid variables, so that we can find their distances. This in turn leads on to a knowledge of the full size of our own star-system, which we call the Galaxy.

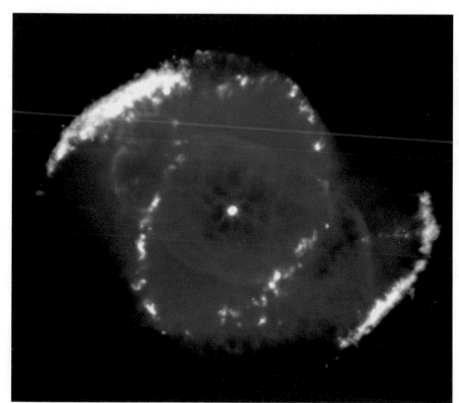

Planetary nebula NGC6543.

THE GALAXY — AND BEYOND

Our Galaxy contains around 100,000 million stars, of which our Sun is one. It is a flattened system, perhaps 100,000 light-years across. The Sun, with its planets, lies almost in the main plane, very nearly 30,000 light-years from the centre of the system.

When we look along the main plane of the system, we see many stars in almost the same line of sight. This produces the appearance of the Milky Way, that lovely band of radiance crossing the night sky. It is made up of stars which look as if they almost touch each other — but this is an illusion. Actually, they are wide apart.

We also know that the Galaxy is rotating. It takes the Sun 225 million years to go once round — a period sometimes called the cosmic year. One cosmic year ago, the most advanced creatures on Earth were amphibians; even the dinosaurs lay in the future. I wonder what the Earth will be like one cosmic year hence?

If we could look at the Galaxy from 'above' or 'below', we would see that it is spiral, like a great Catherine wheel, with the Sun near the edge of one of the spiral arms. This is no surprise, either. Far away in space, we can see other spiral systems.

In the sky we can see patches which we call nebulæ. There is one in Orion, just below the Hunter's Belt. You can see it with the naked eye, and with a telescope it looks like — and is — a mass of glowing gas. It is a

Hubble Space Telescope images of part of the barred spiral galaxy, NGC1365.

Star forming regions in spiral galaxy, NGC353.

stellar nursery, in which fresh stars are being born. And it is one of many.

These are members of our Galaxy. But in Andromeda (the princess of the legend!) there is a different sort of patch. It doesn't look like gas, it is starry, and it proves to be an almost edge-on-spiral galaxy. Other 'starry nebulæ' are face-on galaxies, one dramatic one, near the Great Bear, being aptly called the Whirlpool.

In 1923 a famous American astronomer named Edwin Hubble was using what was then the world's largest telescope — a great reflector, with a 100in mirror, on Mount Wilson in California. He was looking for Cepheids inside the Andromeda Spiral — and he found them. He observed them, found their distances, and realised that they were so far away that they could not possibly be members of our Milky Way system. It followed therefore that the Andromeda Spiral was a separate galaxy.

We now know Andromeda to be larger than our Galaxy — and more than two million light-years away! From these observations, it became clear that our Galaxy is only one of many.

Hubble also found out something else of great significance: that the whole Universe is expanding.

Have you ever listened to an ambulance or a police car coming toward you, sounding its siren? The siren sound will be high-pitched. As the vehicle moves away, the note of the siren drops. During approach, more sound-waves per second are reaching your ear than would be the case if the vehicle were motionless; the wavelength is effectively shortened. During recession, fewer sound-waves per second reach you; the wavelength seems to be lengthened, and the note drops.

QUASARS

Astronomers have uncovered a new enigma in the heavens. They have found strange objects called quasars, now believed to be the cores of very active galaxies, some of which are even more remote than the furthest galaxies. Quasars were first identified by their radio emissions.

I have already explained that light is a wave motion, and visible light ranges from red to blue. If the wavelength is either shorter or longer than this, we can't see it, but we can detect it in other ways. To the short-wave end we have ultra-violet, X-rays and then the very short gamma-rays; to the long-wave end we have infra-red and then radio waves.

You can detect infra-red simply by switching on an electric fire. You can feel the infra-red, as heat, before the bars become hot enough to glow.

Radio waves, on the other hand, are collected by instruments called radio telescopes — not a good name, because a radio telescope doesn't produce a visible picture in the same way as an optical telescope, and you can't look through it. The radio waves are collected and focused, and the end product is usually a trace on a graph. But radio astronomy has become vitally important, and can give us information of a kind which we could never obtain in any other way.

In the 1960s many radio sources in the sky were known, yet they did not seem to come from bright stars. One source was identified with what looked like a faint blue star. When its spectrum was examined (with the great 200in/508cm Palomar telescope at Pasadena, California), astronomers found, to their surprise, that the object was not a star at all. It was more powerful than a galaxy — and the Doppler shifts showed that it was very remote.

Today, quasars are the furthest objects which we can see, and are receding at the fastest speeds.

Light, too, is a wave motion, and we can find the same thing. We call it the Doppler Effect. If a luminous body is approaching, the wavelength will be shortened and the body will appear 'too blue'. When it is receding, it will appear 'too red'.

The actual colour-change is very slight, but with a star, the effect shifts the dark lines either to the red (long-wave) or blue (short-wave) end of the rainbow band. From this, we can tell whether the star is approaching or receding. It was already known before Hubble that the spectrum of a galaxy is made up of a combination of the spectra of millions of stars, and is bound to be a jumble, but the main lines could be identified. Apart from a few relatively nearby galaxies (including the Andromeda Spiral), all the shifts were to the red, which meant that the galaxies were receding away from us — and from each other as well.

Hubble discovered that the further away a galaxy is, the faster it is racing away. The expansion is universal. Today we know of systems which are well over 10,000 million light-years away — and are racing off at over 90 percent of the speed of light! In fact, galaxies tend to occur in groups, and each and every group is receding from every other group.

Where do we on Earth fit into all of this? The answer is that, although we may think ourselves a bit special, the plain truth is that we are in no special position in the Universe!

You can see one problem here. If the rule of 'the further, the faster' holds good, we will eventually come to a distance at which an object is moving away at the full speed of light. We will then be unable to see it, and we will have reached the edge of the observable Universe, though not necessarily the boundary of the Universe itself — if it indeed has one! It seems that this critical distance is between 15,000 million and 20,000 million light-years. But there is considerable uncertainty, and it may even be that there is a major error which may lead to a great deal of rethinking.

One problem is that, apart from visible light, many of the radiations coming from space are blocked out by the Earth's air, so that to study them we have to go into space or send our instruments there. For instance, in 1983 IRAS, the Infra-Red Astronomical Satellite, mapped the entire sky at infra-red wave lengths. And we have sent up a huge optical telescope, the Hubble Telescope, named in honour of Edwin Hubble, which has a 94in (239cm) mirror, and is orbiting round the Earth at a height of over 300 miles (483km), well above most of the atmosphere. The Hubble Telescope can penetrate further into space than any Earth-based telescope, and it has sent back magnificent pictures for astronomers to study.

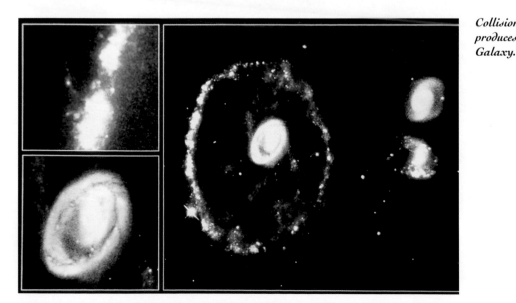

Collision between two galaxies produces the Cartwheel Galaxy.

HOW BIG IS THE UNIVERSE?

Everybody wants to know how far the universe extends — and how it began. At present we can't answer either question. According to our present ideas, the universe came into existence at one particular moment, in a 'Big Bang', around 15,000 million years ago, and has been expanding ever since. Whether this expansion will go on indefinitely, or whether the Universe will finally contract and produce another Big Bang, we don't know. And to be candid, neither do we know why or how the Big Bang happened. We must go on trying to find out.

The other question we all want answered is: Are we alone? Are there 'other beings' in space?

We can be fairly sure that there are none in the Solar System. But if the Sun is an ordinary star, why should not other stars have planets of their own. And why should not those planets be inhabited?

We have found that some stars have 'surrounds' of cool material which may be planet-forming. But not even the Hubble Telescope can show Earth-like planets of other stars. Our only hope may be to pick up radio messages from civilisations far across the Galaxy. Scientist have already attempted exactly that. We have 'listened out' but so far with no success. Perhaps we will succeed . . . one day.

BELOW: Galaxies in the Hubble Deep Field.

FAR RIGHT: The Hertzsprung-Russell diagram: this gives the classification of stars according to their spectral type (of either colour or temperature) and their absolute magnitude.

SOLAR SPECTRUM

We know that stars with different temperatures have different types of spectra, and that by studying them we can discover how powerful a star is and what it is made of.

Star spectra are denoted by letters of the alphabet — in a strange sequence — from very hot stars to cool red stars, marked by the letters O, B, A, F, G, K and M. Early in the 20th century, two astronomers, Ejnar Hertzsprung of Denmark and Henry Norris Russell of America, plotted the stars according to their luminosities and their spectral types and on this page is a typical 'HR' (Hertzsprung-Russell) diagram.

Note that the cool red stars are split into two distinct groups: very powerful giants and very feeble dwarfs. The division is less for hotter stars. (Forget white dwarfs for the purpose of this exercise, as they are totally different).

From this we can work out how a star evolves. It begins by condensing out of a cloud of dust and gas. Gravity makes it shrink. It heats up inside, and joins what we call the Main Sequence (the band from the top left to the bottom right of the 'HR' diagram) unless it is too low in mass, when it simply shines feebly as a red dwarf before losing all its light and heat.

A Sun-like star shines steadily for a long time — thousands of millions of years in the case of the Sun. But when it begins to run short of hydrogen fuel, various nuclear reactions begin — and it moves up to the right of the 'HR' Diagram, becoming a red giant.

When this happens to the Sun, the Earth will be destroyed — possibly around 4,000 million years from now.

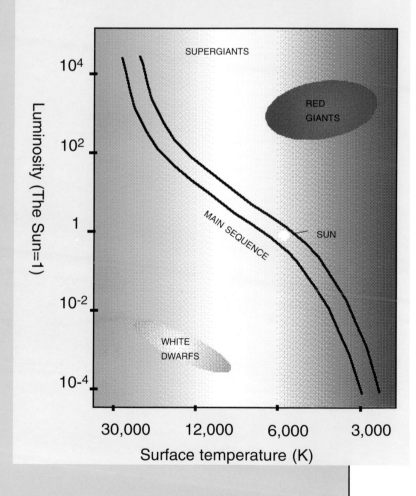

APPENDICES

APPENDIX 1:
The Planets (and their moons)

SUN

Mean distance from Earth 92.9 million miles (149.6 million km)

Light travel time to Earth 8.3 min

Mean angular diameter 32 arc min

Diameter 81,972 miles (1,392,000km)

Mass 1.9891×10^{30}kg

Mean surface temperature 5,800K

Mean internal temperature 15.0×10^6K

Luminosity 3.83×10^{26}W

Spectral type G2

Apparent magnitude -26.8

ABOVE: Diamond ring effect produced by the Moon eclipsing the Sun.

LEFT: Earth rise over the Moon taken by crew of Apollo 8.

EARTH

Mean distance from the Sun 92.9 million miles (149.6 million km)

Orbital period 365.26 days

Axial rotation period 23.93 days

Inclination of axis 23.45°

Inclination of orbit to ecliptic 0° 00' 00"

Eccentricity of orbit 0.017

Equatorial diameter 7,921 miles (12,756km)

Mass 5.9742×10^{24}kg

Mean density 5,500kg/m³

Atmosphere Nitrogen, oxygen

Known satellites One

MOON

Mean distance from Earth 238,712 miles (384,400km)

Synodic period (new moon to new moon) 29.530588 days

Inclination of lunar equator to orbit 6° 41'

Inclination of lunar equator to ecliptic 1° 33'

Orbital eccentricity 0.055

Diameter 2,159 miles (3,476km)

Mass (Earth = 1) 0.0123

Mean density 5,678lb/yd³ (3,340kg/m³)

Brightest magnitude (when full) -12.7

Light travel time is the time it takes light, or any other kind of radiation (see electromagnetic spectrum) from one place to another. Nothing can travel faster than light which travels at 186,000 miles/sec (299,792,458m/sec). Thus, for light to travel from the Sun to the Earth (a distance of 92.9 million miles/149.6 million km) it takes 8.3 minutes.

Mean angular diameter is the angle which the object subtends in the sky. See diagrams.

K is the symbol for the absolute scale of temperature, kelvin. A temperature in kelvin may be converted to one in degrees Celsius by subtracting 273.15. In astronomy, temperatures are usually so extreme that kelvin can be thought of as directly translating to Celsius. For example the temperature of the core (inside) of the Sun is around 15 million degrees. Subtracting 273.15 will not make much difference!

Luminosity is the total energy radiated each second. Compare the luminosity of the Sun (383 million million million million watts to the luminosity of a household light bulb at 100W).

Magnitude. If you go out and look up at the stars, some will appear brighter than others. A measure of this brightness is called the magnitude. Due to the way the ancient Greeks first determined magnitude, the brightest stars always have the smallest number. A star of magnitude 2 is a lot brighter than a star of magnitude 6. Magnitude 6 is about the brightest the naked eye can see in a non-light polluted sky. Stars brighter than magnitude 0 are given a negative number. Thus the brightest star in the sky, Sirius, has apparent magnitude of -1.

The **apparent magnitude** of a star is the magnitude it appears to us on Earth. This does not take into account the size or distance of the star. A star that is intrinsically bright but far away will appear fainter than a dim star that is nearby.

Absolute magnitude is a measure that takes distance into account. It is the magnitude the stars would appear if they were at a common distance (of 10 parsecs). The Sun, our nearest star, has an apparent magnitude of -26.7 and is by far the brightest object in our skies. (Never look directly at the Sun as it can seriously damage your eyes.) But if the Sun was moved away to 10 parsecs, it would only be magnitude 4.9, quite insignificant.

Spectral type is a method of classifying stars according to their spectra (see electromagnetic spectrum). It also gives an idea of the temperature of the star. The classes are:

O	hottest blue stars
B	hot blue stars
A	blue, blue-white stars
F	white stars
G	yellow stars
K	orange stars
M	coolest red stars

The **ecliptic** is the mean plane of the Earth's orbit round the Sun. As we observe from Earth, it can be taken as the apparent path of the Sun through the sky. Most of the planets orbit the Sun in a plane very close to the ecliptic. The angle that a planet's orbit makes with that of the Earth's orbit round the Sun is the inclination of the orbit to the ecliptic.

Eccentricity. The planets orbit the Sun in elliptical orbits with the Sun at one of the foci. However, the orbits are not very elliptical, indeed the Earth has a nearly circular orbit with an eccentricity of only 0.017. A circular orbit would have eccentricity 0. The eccentricity is defined as the ratio of the distance between the focal points of the ellipse to the length of the major axis.

Mean density. Planets are denser at the centre (due to the pressure) than at the surface; the mean density of a planet takes account of this and is the total mass divided by the total volume.

Orbital period is the time a planet takes to orbit the sun. The orbital period of a moon is the time it takes the moon to orbit its parent planet.

Axial rotation is the time it takes a body to spin once on its axis.

Inclination is the angle of a planet's axis between its axis of rotation and the ecliptic.

Albedo is a measure of how dark or bright a planetary body is. An albedo of 1.0 means a very bright, totally reflecting body, while an albedo of 0.0 means a body which is totally black and does not reflect any light at all.

MERCURY

Mean distance from the Sun 36 million miles (57.9 million km)

Orbital period 87.969 days

Axial rotation period 58.646 days

Inclination of axis 0°

Inclination of orbit to ecliptic 7° 00' 16"

Eccentricity of orbit 0.206

Equatorial diameter 3,029 miles (4,878km)

Mass (Earth = 1) 0.055

Mean density 9,231lb/yd³ (5,430 kg/m³)

Brightest magnitude -1.9

Known satellites 0

VENUS

Mean distance from the Sun 67.2 million miles (108.2 million km)

Orbital period 224.70 days

Axial rotation period 243.01 days (retrograde)

Inclination of axis 177°

Inclination of orbit to ecliptic 3° 23' 40"

Eccentricity of orbit 0.007

Equatorial diameter 748 miles (12,104km)

Mass (Earth = 1) 0.8150

Mean density 8,908lb/yd³ (5,240 kg/m³)

Brightest magnitude -4.4

Atmosphere Carbon dioxide

Known satellites 0

Danu Montes, an extinct volcano on Venus. The probe, Mariner II measured the surface temperature on Venus at 800°F (427°C).

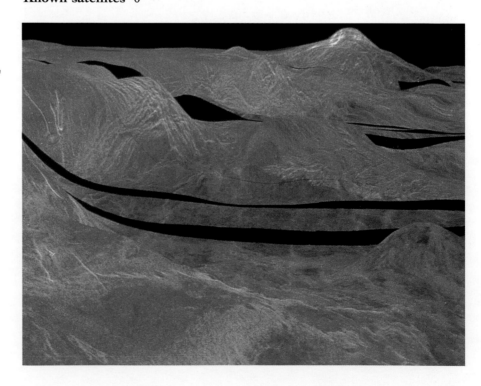

MARS

Viking 2 on Utopian Plain.

Mean distance from the Sun 141.55 million miles (227.94 million km)

Orbital period 686.98 days

Axial rotation period 24.623 days

Inclination of axis 25° 19′

Inclination of orbit to ecliptic 1° 50′ 59″

Eccentricity of orbit 0.093

Equatorial diameter 4,219 miles (6,794km)

Mass (Earth = 1) 0.107

Mean density 6,698lb/yd³ (3,940 kg/m³)

Brightest magnitude -2.0

Atmosphere Carbon dioxide, nitrogen, argon

Known satellites 2

SATELLITES OF MARS

PHOBOS

Discovered by Asaph Hall

Date of discovery 1877

Mean distance from Mars 5,757 miles (9,270km)

Orbital period 7hr 39min

Orbital inclination 1° 1′

Mean diameter 20 x 23 x 17 miles (28km)

Albedo 0.06

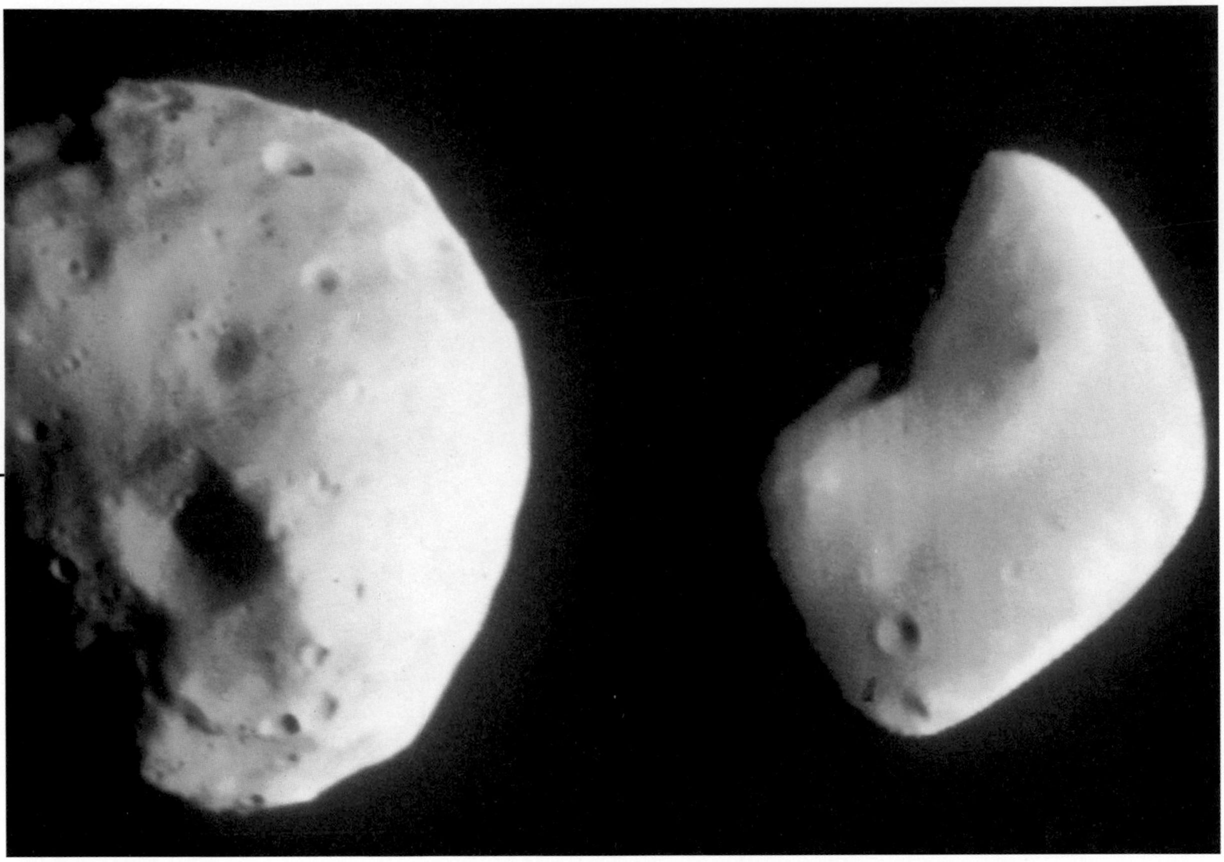

*ABOVE: The two moons of
Mars: Phobos and Deimos.*

*RIGHT: Jupiter, the largest
planet in the solar system.*

DEIMOS

Discovered by Asaph Hall

Date of discovery 1877

Mean distance from Mars 14,531 miles (23,400km)

Orbital period 1.26 days

Orbital inclination 1° 8'

Mean diameter 10 x 12 x 10 miles (16km)

Albedo 0.07

JUPITER

Mean distance from the Sun 483.35 million miles (778.34 million km)

Orbital period 11.86 years

Axial rotation period (equatorial) 9.841hr

Inclination of axis 3.08°

Inclination of orbit to ecliptic 1° 18'

Eccentricity of orbit 0.048

Equatorial diameter 88,794 miles (142,985km)

Mass (Earth = 1) 317.8

Mean density 2,234lb/yd³ (1,314 kg/m³)

Brightest magnitude -2.7

Atmosphere Hydrogen, helium

Known satellites 16

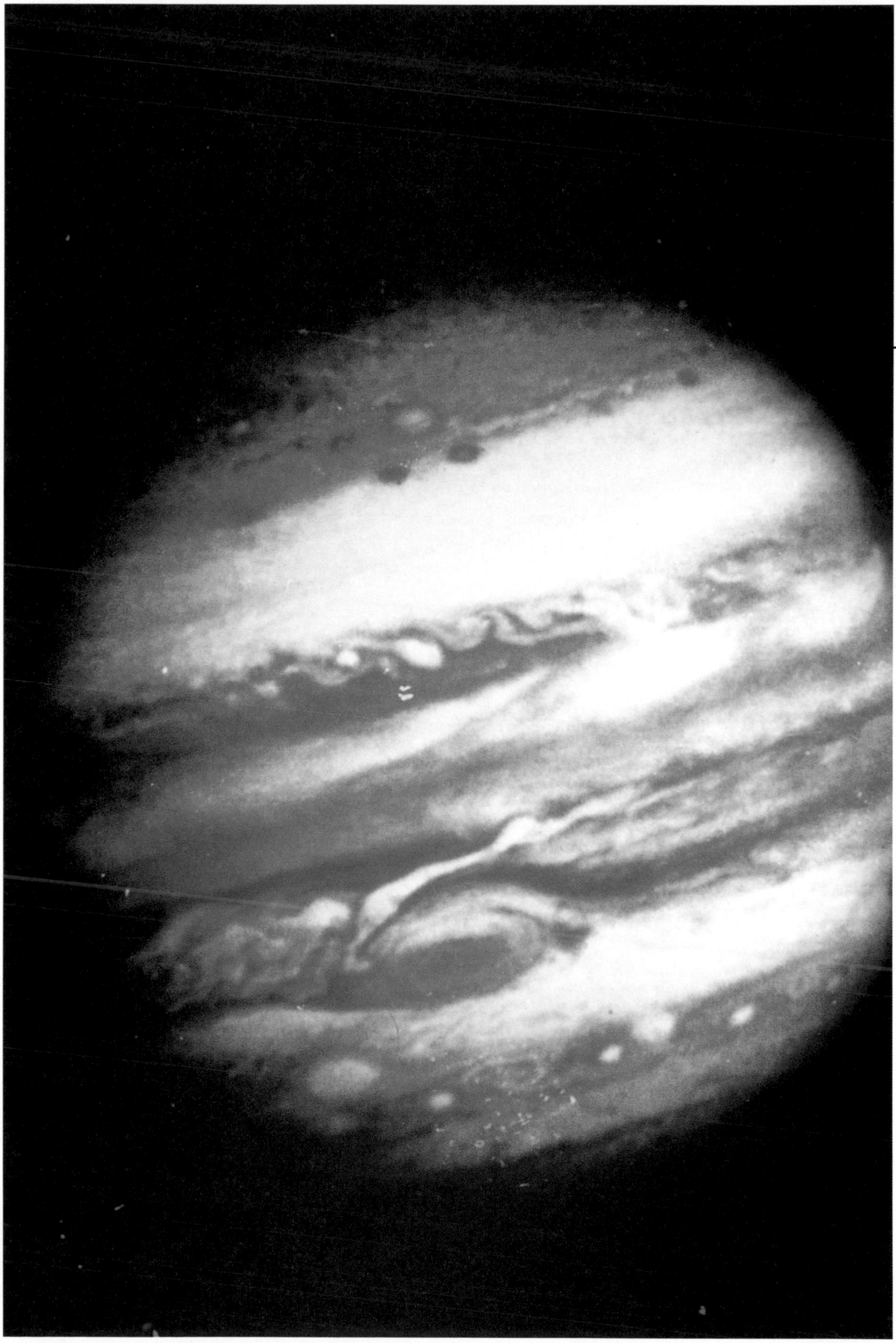

GALILEAN SATELLITES

GANYMEDE

Discovered by Galileo

Date of discovery 1610

Mean distance from Jupiter 664,470 miles (1,070,000km)

Orbital period 7.16 days

Orbital inclination 0.2°

Mean diameter 3,268 miles (5,262km)

Mean density 3,298lb/yd³ (1,940 kg/m³)

Albedo 0.43

CALLISTO

Discovered by Galileo

Date of discovery 1610

Mean distance from Jupiter 1,169,343 miles (1,883,000km)

Orbital period 16.69 days

Orbital inclination 0.5°

Mean diameter 2,981 miles (4,800km)

Mean density 3,077lb/yd³ (1,810 kg/m³)

Albedo 0.17

IO

Discovered by Galileo

Date of discovery 1610

Mean distance from Jupiter 261,814 miles (421,600km)

Orbital period 1.77 days

Orbital inclination 0.0°

Mean diameter 2,254 miles (3,630km

Mean density 6,035lb/yd³ (3,550 kg/m³)

Albedo 0.61

*A volcano on Io, Jupiter's
innermost Galilean moon.*

EUROPA

Discovered by Galileo

Date of discovery 1610

Mean distance from Jupiter 416,629 miles (670,900km)

Orbital period 3.55 days

Orbital inclination 0.5°

Mean diameter 1,949 miles (3,138km)

Mean density 5,049lb/yd³ (2,970 kg/m³)

Albedo 0.64

SATURN

Mean distance from the Sun
884 million miles (1,424 million km)

Orbital period 29.46 years

Axial rotation period 10.233hr

Inclination of axis 26.73°

Inclination of orbit to ecliptic 2.5°

Eccentricity of orbit 0.053

Equatorial diameter 74,853 miles
(120,537km)

Mass (Earth=1) 95.2

Mean density 1,190lb/yd³ (700kg/m³)

Brightest magnitude -0.3

Atmosphere Hydrogen, helium

Known satellites 18

Saturn's rings were first identified by Christiaan Huygens (1629-95), a Dutch physicist and astronomer, in 1655. The rings are made up of small solid particles that revolve around the planet.

SATELLITES OF SATURN

TITAN

Discovered by Huygens

Date of discovery 1655

Mean distance from Saturn 758,800 miles (1,221,900km)

Orbital period 15.95 days

Orbital inclination 0.33°

Mean diameter 5150 km

Mean density 3,196lb/yd³ (1,880kg/m³)

Albedo 0.2

RHEA

Discovered by Cassini

Date of discovery 1672

Mean distance from Saturn 327,627 miles (527,000km)

Orbital period 4.52 days

Orbital inclination 0.35°

Mean diameter 949 miles (1,528km)

Mean density 2,261lb/yd³ (1,330kg/m³)

Albedo 0.7

RIGHT: Iapetus, one of the moons of Saturn.

IAPETUS

Discovered by Cassini

Date of discovery 1671

Mean distance from Saturn
2,211,381 miles 3,561,000km

Orbital period 79.33 days

Orbital inclination 14.72°

Mean diameter 892 miles
(1,436km)

Mean density 2,057lb/yd³
(1,210kg/m³)

Albedo 0.5–0.05

DIONE

Discovered by Cassini

Date of discovery 1684

Mean distance from Saturn 234,428 miles (377,500km)

Orbital period 2.74 days

Orbital inclination 0.02°

Mean diameter 696 miles (1,120km)

Mean density 2,431lb/yd³ (1,430kg/m³)

Albedo 0.7

TETHYS

Discovered by Cassini

Date of discovery 1684

Mean distance from Saturn 183,009 (294,700km)

Orbital period 1.89 days

Orbital inclination 1.86°

Mean diameter 1,072 x 1,056 x 653 miles (1,052km)

Mean density 2,057lb/yd³ (1,210kg/m³)

Albedo 0.9

MIMAS

Discovered by Herschel

Date of discovery 1789

Mean distance from Saturn 115,196 miles (185,500km)

Orbital period 0.94 days

Orbital inclination 1.53°

Mean diameter 418 x 392 x 237miles (382km)

Mean density 1,989lb/yd³ (1,170 kg/m³)

Albedo 0.5

ENCELADUS

Discovered by Herschel

Date of discovery 1789

Mean distance from Saturn
147,798 miles (238,000km)

Orbital period 1.37 days

Orbital inclination 0.02°

Mean diameter 512 x 494 x 304 miles
(490km)

Mean density 2,108lb/yd³ (1,240kg/m³)

Albedo 1.0

URANUS

Discovered by Herschel

Date of discovery 1781

Mean distance from the Sun
1,782 m miles (2,869.6 million km)

Orbital period 84.01 years

Axial rotation period (internal)
17.24hr

Inclination of axis 97.86°

Inclination of orbit to ecliptic
0.773°

Eccentricity of orbit 0.043

Equatorial diameter 31,744 miles
(51,118km)

Mass (Earth = 1) 14.5

Mean density 2,210lb/yd³ (1,300kg/m³)

Brightest magnitude +5.6

Atmosphere Hydrogen, helium

Known satellites 15

SATELLITES OF URANUS

TITANIA

Discovered by Herschel

Date of discovery 1787

Mean distance from Uranus 270,694 miles (435,900km)

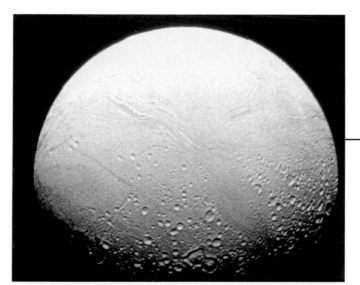

*TOP: Enceladus, another
moon belonging to Saturn.*

ABOVE: Uranus' rings.

Orbital period 8.706 days

Orbital inclination 0.14°

Mean diameter 987 miles (1,580km)

Mean density 2,720lb/yd³ (1,600kg/m³)

Albedo 0.28

OBERON

Discovered by Herschel

Date of discovery 1787

Mean distance from Uranus 361,733 miles (582,500km)

Orbital period 13.46 days

Orbital inclination 0.10°

Mean diameter 946 miles (1,524km)

Mean density 932lb/yd³ (1,500kg/m³)

Albedo 0.24

UMBRIEL

Discovered by Lassell

Date of discovery 1851

Mean distance from Uranus 165,372 miles (266,300km)

Orbital period 4.144 days

Orbital inclination 0.36°

Mean diameter 728 miles (1,172km)

Mean density 2,550lb/yd³ (1,500kg/m³⁾

Albedo 0.19

ARIEL

Discovered by Lassell

Date of discovery 1851

Mean distance from Uranus 118,611 miles (191,000km)

Orbital period 2.520 days

Orbital inclination 0.31°

Mean diameter 719 miles (1,158km)

Mean density 2,720lb/yd³
(1,600kg/m³)

Albedo 0.40

MIRANDA

Discovered by Kuiper

Date of discovery 1948

Mean distance from Uranus
80,357 miles (129,400km)

Orbital period 1.413 days

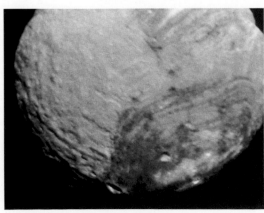

RIGHT: Miranda, one of Uranus' fifteen known satellites.

FAR RIGHT, TOP: The planet Neptune seen from 3.7 million miles (6 million km) by Voyager.

FAR RIGHT, BELOW: Triton, the largest of Neptune's eight known satellites.

Orbital inclination 4.22°
Mean diameter 298 miles (480km)
Mean density 2,210lb/yd³
(1,300kg/m³)
Albedo 0.34

NEPTUNE
Discovered by Le Verrier
Date of discovery 1846
Mean distance from the Sun
2,792.5 million miles
(4,496.7 million km)
Orbital period 164.8 years
Axial rotation period (int) 16.11hr
Inclination of axis 29.56°
Inclination of orbit to ecliptic 1.77°
Eccentricity of orbit 0.010
Equatorial diameter 30,757 miles
(49,528km)
Mass (Earth = 1) 17.2
Mean density 2,992lb/yd³
(1,760kg/m³)
Brightest magnitude +7.7
Atmosphere Hydrogen, helium
Known satellites 8

SATELLITES OF NEPTUNE

TRITON
Discovered by Lassell
Date of discovery 1846
Mean distance from Neptune
220,331 miles (354,800km)
Orbital period 5.877 days
(retrograde)
Orbital inclination 157.4°
Mean diameter 1,680 miles
(2,705km)
Mean density 3,502lb/yd³
(2,060kg/m³)
Albedo 0.7

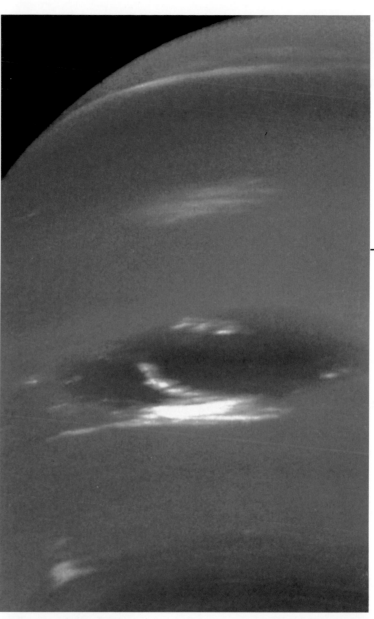

NEREID

Discovered by Kuiper

Date of discovery 1949

Mean distance from Neptune 3,423,573 miles (5,513,000km)

Orbital period 360.14 days

Orbital inclination 27.2°

Mean diameter 211 miles (340km)

Albedo 0.16

PLUTO

Discovered by Clyde W. Tombaugh

Date of discovery 18 February 1930

Mean distance from the Sun 5,913.52 x 6.2 million miles (10^6km)

Orbital period 248.54

Axial rotational period 6.3872 days

Inclination of axis 117.56°

Inclination of orbit to ecliptic 17.148°

Eccentricity of orbit 0.250

Equatorial diameter 1,441 (2,320km)

Mass (Earth = 1) 0.003

Mean density 1,870lb/yd³ (1,100kg/m³)

Brightest magnitude +13.8

Atmospheric composition Methane, nitrogen

Known satellites 1

SATELLITE OF PLUTO

CHARON

Discovered by J. Christy

Date of discovery 1978

Mean distance from Pluto 12,196 miles (19,640km)

Orbital period 6.387

Orbital inclination 98.80°

Mean diameter 745 miles (1,200km)

Mean density 3,400lb/yd³ (2,000kg/m³)

Albedo 0.5

APPENDIX 2:
LIST OF CONSTELLATIONS

Andromeda	Andromeda	**Leo**	The Lion
Antlia	The Airpump	**Leo Minor**	The Little Lion
Apus	The Bird of Paradise	**Lepus**	The Hare
Aquarius	The Water-bearer	**Libra**	The Balance
Aquila	The Eagle	**Lupus**	The Wolf
Ara	The Altar	**Lynx**	The Lynx
Aries	The Ram	**Lyra**	The Lyre
Auriga	The Charioteer	**Mensa**	The Table
Bootes	The Herdsman	**Microscopium**	The Microscope
Caelum	The Graving Tool	**Monoceros**	The Unicorn
Camelopardalis	The Giraffe	**Musca**	The Southern Fly
Cancer	The Crab	**Norma**	The Rule
Canes Venatici	The Hunting Dogs	**Octans**	The Octant
Canis Major	The Great Dog	**Ophiuchus**	The Serpent-bearer
Canis Minor	The Little Dog	**Orion**	Orion
Capricornus	The Sea-Goat	**Pavo**	The Peacock
Carina	The Keel	**Pegasus**	The Flying Horse
Cassiopeia	Cassiopeia	**Perseus**	Perseus
Centaurus	The Centaur	**Phoenix**	The Phoenix
Cepheus	Cepheus	**Pictor**	The Painter
Cetus	The Whale	**Pisces**	The Fishes
Chamaeleon	The Chameleon	**Piscis Austrinus**	The Southern Fish
Circinus	The Compasses	**Puppis**	The Poop
Columba	The Dove	**Pyxis**	The Compass
Coma Berenices	Berenice's Hair	**Reticulum**	The Net
Corona Australis	The Southern Crown	**Sagitta**	The Arrow
Corona Borealis	The Northern Crown	**Sagittarius**	The Archer
Corvus	The Crow	**Scorpius**	The Scorpion
Crater	The Cup	**Sculptor**	The Sculptor
Crux	The Southern Cross	**Scutum**	The Shield
Cygnus	The Swan	**Serpens**	The Serpent
Delphinus	The Dolphin	**Sextans**	The Sextant
Dorado	The Swordfish	**Taurus**	The Bull
Draco	The Dragon	**Telescopium**	The Telescope
Equuleus	The Foal	**Triangulum**	The Triangle
Eridanus	The River	**Triangulum Australe**	The Southern Triangle
Fornax	The Furnace	**Tucana**	The Toucan
Gemini	The Twins	**Ursa Major**	The Great Bear
Grus	The Crane	**Ursa Minor**	The Little Bear
Hercules	Hercules	**Vela**	The Sails
Horologium	The Clock	**Virgo**	The Virgin
Hydra	The Watersnake	**Volans**	The Flying Fish
Hydrus	The Little Snake	**Vulpecula**	The Fox
Indus	The Indian		
Lacerta	The Lizard		

APPENDIX 3:
THE 20 BRIGHTEST STARS

Star	Constellation	Name	Apparent mag	Absolute mag	Distance (light years)
1 **CMa**	Ursa Major	Sirius	-1.46	0.7	8.7
2 **Car**	Carina	Canopus	-0.72	-5.5	300
3 **Cen**	Centaurus	Rigil Kentaurus	-0.27	4.6	4.4
4 **Boo**	Boötes	Arcturus	-0.04	-0.3	36
5 **Lyr**	Lyra	Vega	0.03	0.3	26
6 **Aur**	Auriga	Capella	0.08	0.1	45
7 **Ori**	Orion	Rigel	0.12	-7.0	850
8 **CMi**	Canis Minor	Procyon	0.38	2.8	11
9 **Eri**	Eridanus	Achernar	0.46	-1.3	75
10 **Ori**	Orion	Betelgeuse	0.50	-5.5	650
11 **Cen**	Centaurus	Hadar	0.61	-4.3	300
12 **Aql**	Aquila	Altair	0.77	2.1	17
13 **Cru**	Crux	Acrux	0.79	-3.8	270
14 **Tau**	Taurus	Aldebaran	0.85	-0.2	65
15 **Sco**	Scorpius	Antares	0.96	-4.5	400
16 **Vir**	Virgo	Spica	0.98	-3.2	220
17 **Gem**	Gemini	Pollux	1,14	0.7	35
18 **PsA**	Piscis Austrinus	Fomalhaut	1.16	1.8	22
19 **Cru**	Crux	Mimosa	1.25	-4.0	370
20 **Cyg**	Cygnus	Deneb	1.25	-7.0	1,500

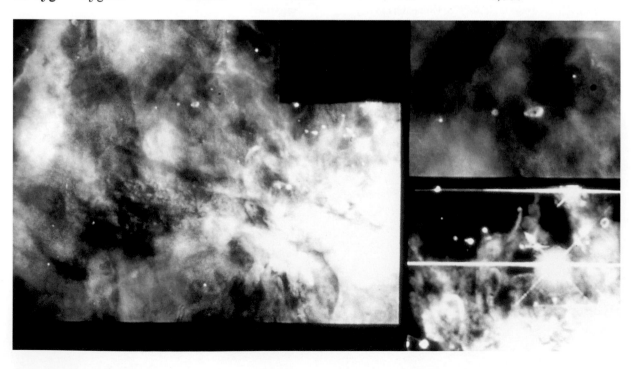

APPENDIX 4:
THE STAR CHARTS

If you go out and look up at the sky, the stars appear to be on the inside of an upturned bowl which arches over the flat land as far as you can see. This apparent bowl is called the celestial sphere, because if you could see through the ground at your feet, the bowl would continue into a sphere surrounding the Earth.

In order to map the positions of the stars, astronomers use Right Ascension (RA) and declination (dec). Right Ascension is the 'longitude' of a star on the celestial sphere. It is measured from the point where the ecliptic crosses the equator (called the First Point of Aries), and is measured in hours, minutes and seconds. It takes the Earth 24 hours to rotate once on its axis, so it takes the sky 24 hours to apparently rotate 360° round the Earth. Thus one hour is equivalent to 15° of sky.

The 'latitude' of a star is measured north or south of the equator. The equator is the circle on the celestial sphere which would appear if the Earth's own equator was extended outwards. Thus if you were standing on the equator, a star directly overhead would have zero declination.

Stars north of the equator have positive declination, thus the north pole star, Polaris, has a declination of +90°, while a star overhead at the south pole would have a declination of -90°.

The star maps show the whole sky, but of course you cannot see all the stars from one location. It depends what latitude you are observing from. For star watchers in the northern hemisphere, for example, the southern constellations round the south pole will never rise above the horizon.

What you will be able to see during any particular night will depend on your latitude and also on the time of year. Different constellations are visible at different times of the year because the Earth orbits the Sun. If the Sun is between the Earth and a certain constellation, then it is not visible at night.

Thus to use the charts, the declination equivalent to your latitude is what will appear directly above your head. At latitude 50° north, stars with declination +50° will be overhead, while if you are at latitude 30° south, the stars overhead will have declination -30°.

An idea of the section of sky visible on a clear night for each time of year is given with each chart.

FAR LEFT: The Orion Nebula imaged by the HST.

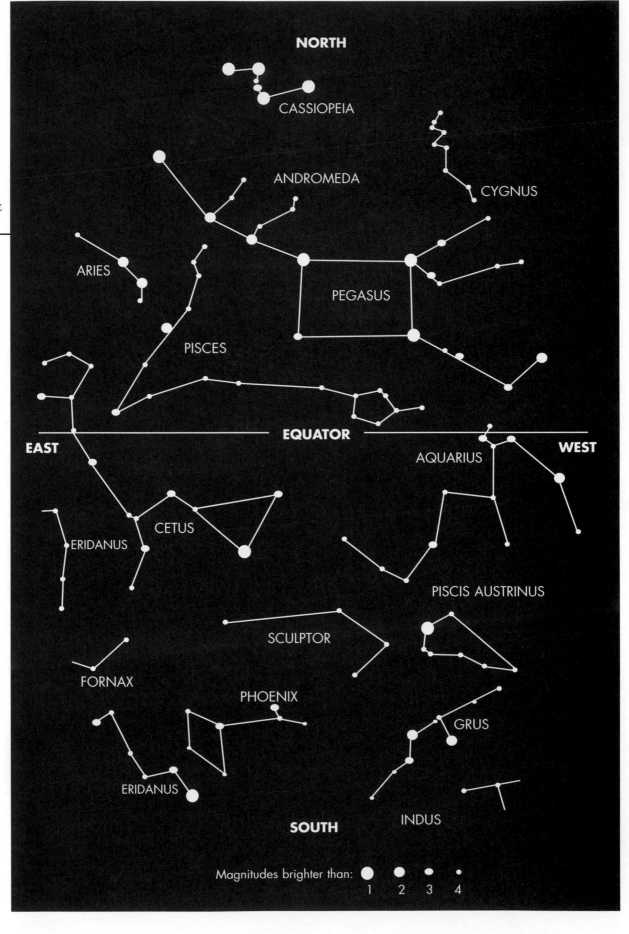

NORTH

CASSIOPEIA

ANDROMEDA

CYGNUS

ARIES

PEGASUS

PISCES

EQUATOR

EAST

WEST

AQUARIUS

CETUS

ERIDANUS

PISCIS AUSTRINUS

SCULPTOR

FORNAX

PHOENIX

GRUS

ERIDANUS

INDUS

SOUTH

Magnitudes brighter than:

1 2 3 4

The night sky,
September to
November.

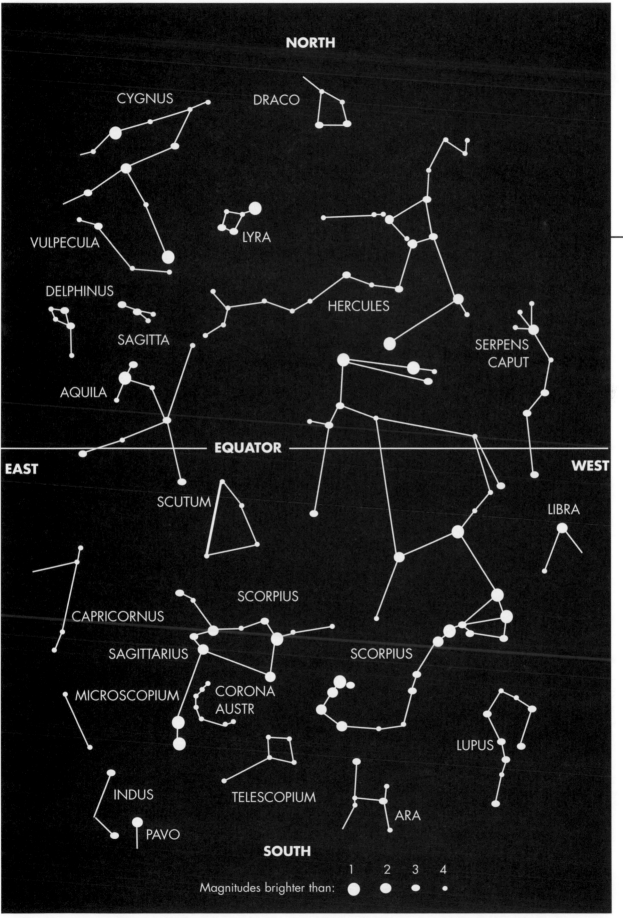

NORTH

CYGNUS

DRACO

VULPECULA

LYRA

DELPHINUS

SAGITTA

HERCULES

AQUILA

SERPENS
CAPUT

EQUATOR

EAST

WEST

SCUTUM

LIBRA

CAPRICORNUS

SCORPIUS

SAGITTARIUS

SCORPIUS

MICROSCOPIUM

CORONA
AUSTR

LUPUS

INDUS

TELESCOPIUM

PAVO

ARA

SOUTH

1   2   3   4

Magnitudes brighter than: ● ● ● ·

*The night sky,
June to August.*

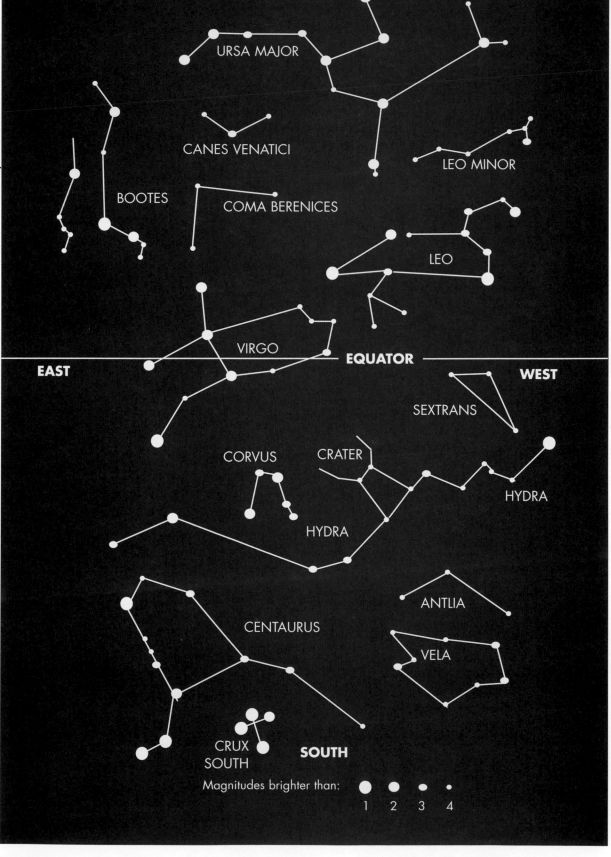

NORTH

URSA MAJOR

CANES VENATICI

LEO MINOR

BOOTES

COMA BERENICES

LEO

VIRGO

EQUATOR

EAST

WEST

SEXTRANS

CORVUS

CRATER

HYDRA

HYDRA

ANTLIA

CENTAURUS

VELA

CRUX
SOUTH

SOUTH

Magnitudes brighter than:

1   2   3   4

The night sky,
March to May.

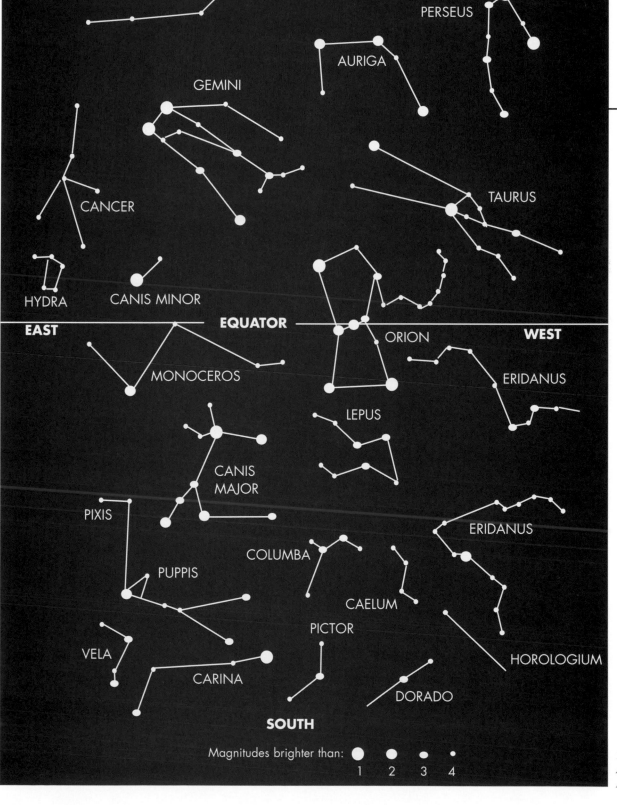

NORTH

LYNX

PERSEUS

AURIGA

GEMINI

CANCER

TAURUS

HYDRA

CANIS MINOR

EAST

EQUATOR

ORION

WEST

MONOCEROS

ERIDANUS

LEPUS

CANIS MAJOR

PIXIS

ERIDANUS

COLUMBA

PUPPIS

CAELUM

VELA

PICTOR

CARINA

HOROLOGIUM

DORADO

SOUTH

Magnitudes brighter than: ● ● ● ·
1 2 3 4

The night sky,
December to
February.

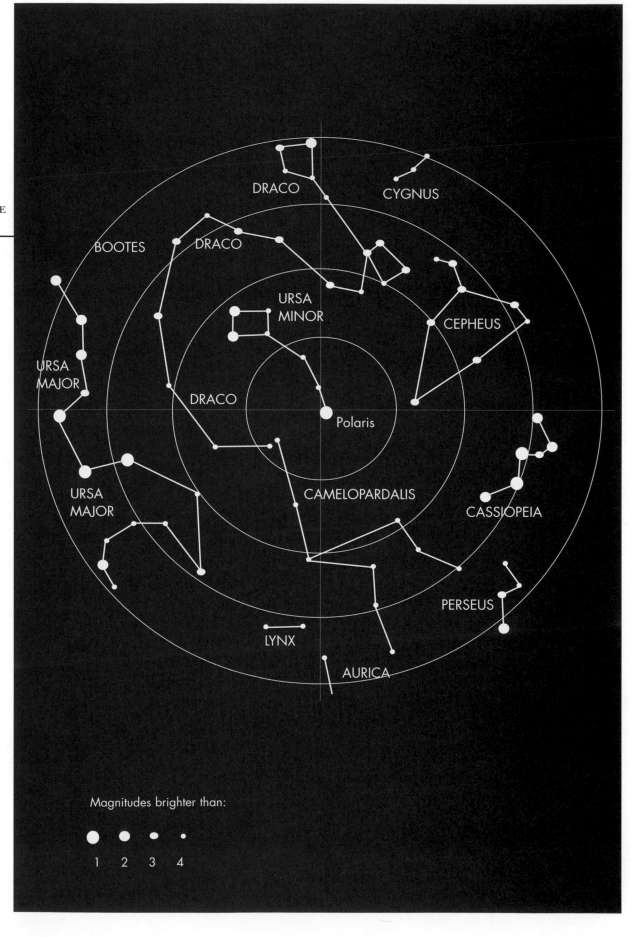

Magnitudes brighter than:

1   2   3   4

*North polar sky,
northern autumn.*

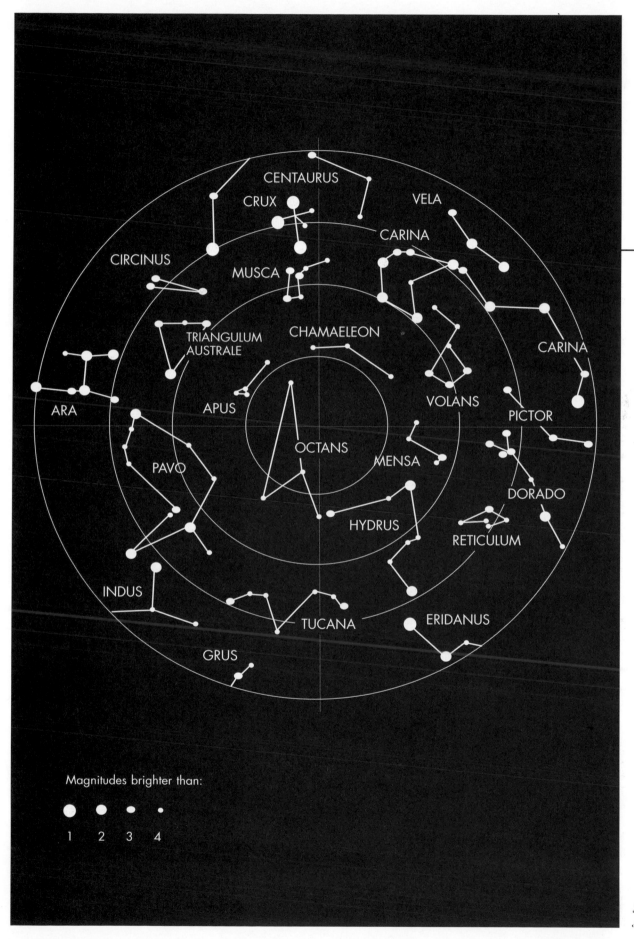

CENTAURUS
CRUX
VELA
CARINA
CIRCINUS
MUSCA
CARINA
TRIANGULUM AUSTRALE
CHAMAELEON
APUS
ARA
VOLANS
PICTOR
OCTANS
MENSA
PAVO
DORADO
HYDRUS
RETICULUM
INDUS
ERIDANUS
TUCANA
GRUS

Magnitudes brighter than:

○ ● ● •
1 2 3 4

South polar sky, southern winter.

ACKNOWLEDGEMENTS

The Publishers would like to thank Nigel Blundell who co-ordinated and edited this book and Pam Spence, editor of *Astronomy Now,* who researched the photographs and produced much of the additional material and data. *Astronomy Now* is published by Polestar Publications Ltd available monthly from all good newsagents; subscription information is available within the magazine.

PICTURE CREDITS

The Publishers would like to thank all who contributed photographs to this book:
Astronomy Now: 43, 44, 45, 48, 55
Joshua Allden: 4, 22, 27 (top), 58
Alan Dowdell: 20 (both), 27 (bottom), 41, 42 (both), 57, 80

Dee Levers: 9, 10, 11, 12
Meade 19
NASA: 1, 24, 25 (both), 26, 38, 56
NASA/JPL: 2, 13, 28, 29, 30, 32 (both), 33, 34 (both), 35, 36 (all), 37, 60, 61, 62, 63, 64, 65, 66 , 67(both), 68, 69 (both)
NASA/STSCI: 46 (both), 47, 49, 50, 51, 53, 54, 72
Orion 18
Pam Spence: 15, 16,
Alex Vincent: 39
Vixen 17 (all)